SMSG   The Making of a Curriculum

SMSG   The Making of a Curriculum

by William Wooton

New Haven and London, Yale University Press, 1965

Copyright © 1965 by Yale University.
Designed by Sally Hargrove,
set in Baskerville type,
and printed in the United States of America by
The Carl Purington Rollins Printing-Office
of the Yale University Press.
Distributed in Canada by McGill University Press.
All rights reserved. This book may not be
reproduced, in whole or in part, in any form
(except by reviewers for the public press),
without written permission from the publishers.
Library of Congress catalog card number: 65–12550

Preface

The decade 1955–65 has witnessed a vast upheaval in parts of the secondary school curriculum. In particular, high school physics, chemistry, biology, and mathematics have all been subjected to intense scrutiny by subject-matter specialists, and far-reaching recommendations for changes in the content and teaching of courses in these subjects have resulted. It is difficult to find another decade in the history of education where so much attention has been devoted to such a narrow part of the curriculum by so many recognized authorities at the research level in the various sciences. However, while many of those associated with education below the college level are familiar with the recommendations and sample textbooks produced by the many committees, commissions, and groups currently working with curriculum reform, too few persons are aware of how these various organizations came to be and what they represent.

This brief book provides a description of the origin and activities of one of these groups, the School Mathematics Study Group (SMSG), over the first four years of its existence. While SMSG is not necessarily representative of all curriculum study groups, it is safe to say that many of the experiences of SMSG are similar to those of other such groups. Certainly the goals of all of them are the same, namely, a modification of the existing curriculum at the high school

v

level and below in the subject area with which they are concerned. Moreover, most of them have discovered that the best way to accomplish this modification is to provide a model of the kind of improved curriculum they desire, and to provide this model in the form of sample textbooks. Still another of the similarities most of these groups display lies in the way they seek collaboration between experts in subject-matter fields and experts in teaching children at the appropriate grade levels. The majority of the persons associated with SMSG consider this collaboration the most important single factor in such success as SMSG has achieved in moving toward its goals.

In reading this account, there are a number of things of which the reader should be aware. For one thing, the chief purpose of this book is to describe the activities and *modus operandi* of SMSG. In describing these, some mention of technical mathematical ideas is unavoidable, but such references have been kept to a minimum. The book is addressed to any person, mathematically trained or otherwise, with a curiosity about how a group such as SMSG undertakes to influence the curriculum of the schools of the United States.

Secondly, no documentation of facts is provided. Such footnotes as occur are largely for the purpose of directing attention to the lists of names (in the Appendix) of persons associated with certain aspects of the work of SMSG. For details such as dates, agendas, and outcomes of meetings of committees, panels, and writers, the files of SMSG provided all the information used. For other matters, such as, for example, the specific method of procedure used by a writing team, information was obtained from the person directly in charge of the activity, either by oral interview or by means of written description. Allied with a description of the activities of sample-textbook writing teams there is, at a more speculative level, a rationale for the contents of the books, and for this I am indebted largely to written materials provided by some of the writers, which are contained in SMSG files.

Preface

Another aspect of the contents of this book of which the reader should be apprised is that, without making a detailed study thereof, I have described the state of mathematics education in this country from about 1890 until the present time as I envisage it. This description is a distillation of much reading, many conversations with persons engaged in the field of mathematics education through the period, and my own firsthand experience in the enterprise, both as a student and a teacher, over more than half those years. However, it is only fair to reiterate that scholarly research has *not* been employed, and the reader should not read into remarks concerning these matters more than my own opinion. For example, statistics regarding numbers of qualified teachers of mathematics at such-and-such a grade level in such-and-such a decade are kept deliberately vague. It is precisely because no attempt was made to research this part of the material in any real sense that no citation of sources is given in the manuscript. To have cited one source without having made an honest effort to evaluate all available sources, and without having made some judgments relative to the credibility thereof, would be to give a spurious impression of the validity of that which was documented.

Many readers of this book will also remark a noticeable absence of specificity with regard to who did what in the many writing activities described. The lack of such explicit information is not assignable to whim on my part, but, rather, stems from the nature of SMSG writing sessions. There is simply no way to ascertain exactly who was chiefly responsible for each section of each publication. Moreover, I have even refrained from specifically identifying individuals (other than subgroup chairmen) working at each grade level. This is partly because many persons worked at more than one such level, but chiefly because no useful purpose would seem to be served by trying to associate groups of fifteen to thirty persons with a given publication.

I owe a very real debt to the many busy mathematicians,

mathematics teachers, supervisors, and others associated with SMSG who read the preliminary version of this book and took valuable time to offer helpful advice. Most of all, I am grateful to Professor E. G. Begle of Stanford University, Director of SMSG, without whose cooperation I could not have written it.

W. W.

Northridge, California
February 1965

Contents

Preface

1. The Origins of SMSG   1

2. First Writing Session   17

3. First Year   44

4. Second Writing Session   61

5. Tryout and Revision of Sample Textbooks   82

6. From Yale to Stanford   105

7. Reorganization   124

8. Reactions to SMSG   135

Appendix   145

Index   173

1 The Origins of SMSG

The School Mathematics Study Group (SMSG) did not come into existence until 1958 but its story begins earlier. In order to obtain a clear perspective of the nature of the Group and its work, it will prove helpful to consider briefly some relatively recent history of the American high school, and the implications of this history for high school mathematics.

Early in this century, many people in the United States began to question the prevailing tenet that a high school education was reserved for the elite, and they began to view the high school as a possible vehicle for the education of the masses. This increased interest in the nature and function of secondary education derived from a number of factors. The assembly line seemed to be diminishing the need for some of the skills that demanded long apprenticeship, while at the same time white-collar jobs that demanded more formal education were growing in number. There seemed little purpose in a young man's foregoing additional formal education in favor of apprenticing to a trade that might cease to exist in a short time. Another factor was the large number of youths who were either immigrants or first-generation children of immigrants and whose assimilation into the American culture was a very real problem. A third factor was the wave of social conscience that swept across the country during the late 1800s and early 1900s. Overcrowded cities, low wages, monopolistic tendencies, and political corruption led to the enactment of such legislation as the Pure Food and Drug Act, the Hepburn Act, the Federal Reserve Act, and others. All these developments had implications for the secondary schools.

By 1900, the need for the expansion of the secondary education facilities of the country was obvious, as was the fact that the purpose of the high school could no longer be solely that of preparing students for college. The high school curriculum had to be re-examined in the light of changed objectives. Less than ten years before, in 1893, the National Council of Education's Committee of Ten, a group of distinguished educators, had issued its report on secondary school education, to a great extent reaffirming the value of existing curricula (the classics, history, mathematics, and modern, i.e. European, languages) but helping pave the way for curriculum revision. Within a generation, a dramatic change in the thinking of educators took place.

In 1914, the National Education Association appointed a Commission on the Reorganization of the Secondary School. The function of this Commission was to reconsider the goals of the nation's high schools. Four years later, in 1918, the Commission issued a report centering around seven principles. These came to be known as the Seven Cardinal Principles of Secondary Education. The Commission asserted that secondary education should stress health, vocation, citizenship, ethical character, estimable use of leisure, worthy home life, and command of the fundamental processes, factors they deemed basic to the life of the citizenry of a twentieth-century democracy. This report had such a profound effect on the subsequent design of the secondary school curriculum of this country that it has been called the most influential single document in the history of American education.

As long as the high school was a vehicle for the preparation of students for college, the mathematics offerings were few and classical. Algebra, geometry, trigonometry, and solid geometry constituted the bulk of the mathematics curriculum, and, de-

The Origins of SMSG

pending on the course of study elected, students were required to complete from two to four years in these subjects. Following the statement of the Seven Cardinal Principles came a slow but steady change in the course offerings, and the number of mathematics courses required of each student was gradually reduced. While the Seven Cardinal Principles did not have many pronouncements to make on specific course content, they could, like tea leaves in the bottom of a cup, be interpreted. Accordingly, if a subject did not seem to affect potentially the health, vocation, citizenship, and so on, of the student, it was judged unworthy of a place in the curriculum. This kind of interpretation led to highly polemical attacks on the classical courses in algebra and geometry and engendered a host of new offerings: general mathematics, basic mathematics, consumer mathematics, shop mathematics, commercial mathematics, and others.

Another change in the old patterns occurred. Until about 1920, academic and research scientists had maintained a more or less fruitful dialogue with their subject-matter colleagues in the high schools. These scientists had contributed to the development of courses, to the design of learning aids such as laboratory equipment, and had been partially responsible for the textbooks used in the high schools. The rapid growth in size of the secondary school classroom and the consequent new problems of the high school teacher contributed to his gradual estrangement from the research scientist. The scientist, for his part, could no longer find the time or the means to continue the dialogue because of the explosive increase in productive research. Like Alice's Cheshire cat, the scientists faded from the secondary scene until nothing remained but a grin.[1]

Throughout the years 1920–50, then, the mathematics offerings in the secondary schools of the United States reflected the influence of a societal, utilitarian philosophy. In most mathe-

---

1. This is, of course, true only in the large. Some very excellent scientists here and there in the country continued to work with secondary school teachers.

3

matics courses, emphasis was placed on mathematical procedures of use to consumers, government, industry, and commerce, and less and less time was devoted to the theoretical considerations on which such procedures were based. Attention was devoted largely to the establishment of skills—the ability to perform certain routine computations. The failure of a student to achieve a certain level of proficiency in this area was the signal for his enrollment in a remedial mathematics program. Remedial mathematics courses had become an everyday part of the high school curriculum by 1950.

As another consequence of the utilitarian viewpoint, the textbooks used in high school mathematics classes changed over the years. Textbooks published in the late 1800s and early 1900s were written for a select population and were uncompromising in the intellectual demands they made on the student. As high school enrollment changed in number and needs, the mathematics included in the textbooks came to be selected more and more on the basis of teachability. Because of real or fancied reading difficulties on the part of students, exposition in many textbooks was reduced to an absolute minimum. A typical lesson might consist of two or three solved samples followed by a sequence of practice exercises, and students were expected to apply the steps exhibited in the samples to get answers in the exercises. The degree of success attained by a student using such texts was a direct function of the student's ability to identify a problem by type and then to apply the appropriate symbol manipulations to obtain the designated answer. The only requisites for successful achievement in high school mathematics were, in many cases, a good memory and a willingness to follow directions.

In addition to changes in course content and textbooks, the years from 1930 to 1950 witnessed a change in the qualifications of mathematics teachers. Because of the increased number of students enrolled in academic mathematics classes—this despite a drop in the percentage of students enrolled in such classes—the demand for trained teachers of mathematics far

The Origins of SMSG

exceeded the supply. It had become increasingly possible for a college graduate with a major in mathematics to find employment in areas other than high school teaching, and many such areas offered greater remuneration. Furthermore, the nature of the course content in most high school mathematics classes offered little of interest to a person who had spent four or more years learning advanced mathematics. As the availability of adequately prepared teachers of mathematics declined, the demand for them rose, and large numbers of poorly trained persons came forward. By 1950, many high school mathematics teachers were teaching at or beyond the level that they had successfully completed as students. Persons whose training had been in physical education, English, history, or homemaking were pressed into service as teachers of mathematics. The natural consequence was that students were being poorly trained and, perhaps more important, negative attitudes toward mathematics were being instilled in the minds of countless numbers of American youth.

In the eyes of many thoughtful members of the mathematical community, the picture of mathematics education in American high schools in 1950 was not a pretty one. In particular, they were dissatisfied both with the content of the course offerings and with the spirit in which the material was presented. They were convinced that the traditional subject matter was inappropriate to the times. Worse, they were alarmed at what they felt were the implications for the future. In their opinion there was undue emphasis being placed on skills, an unnecessary preoccupation with the immediate usefulness of what was taught, and an unfortunate distortion of the students' ideas as to the nature of mathematics. They believed that these things were actually dangerous to the future welfare of the country.

It is difficult to ascribe responsibility for the situation. It was clearly not the fault of the teachers that many of them were having to teach a subject they had not been trained to teach, and that others were bound to a curriculum they found repugnant. Neither could the administrators of the schools be blamed. They were confronted with students whom they had to supply with teachers, and they did the best they could with the resources available. Since most principals and superintendents were not specialists in mathematics, they could not be expected to pass judgment on the quality of the mathematics taught in their schools. They relied largely on the textbooks for guidance in course offerings. Textbook writers wrote textbooks for commercial distribution, and they found that the books that sold the most copies were those that were least demanding on students and teachers alike. They wrote accordingly. Lastly, it would be unfair to censure the teacher-training institutions of the country, whose staffs were engaged in a herculean effort to establish public schools appropriate to the needs of the millions of people in twentieth-century America. To them, mathematics was but one of a host of subjects in the curriculum, and, according to the pragmatic philosophy to which many of them adhered, not a very important one. Such authority as the departments of education had over mathematics education in the schools fell to them primarily through the default of their colleagues in the mathematics departments.

If blame has to be placed somewhere, perhaps it should be on the research mathematicians of the country who, as a group, abandoned any interest in high school mathematics or the training of teachers of high school mathematics in favor of concentrating entirely on research. But blaming them would not seem to be wholly justified either. The mathematicians had work of compelling importance to accomplish in their own specialties, work that could not be done by others.

Regardless of who or what was responsible for the situation as it existed at mid-century, the decade 1950–60 witnessed the explosive growth of a movement bent on improving the teaching of mathematics in American schools. Even before 1950, a small group of secondary schools and colleges began working with the College Entrance Examination Board (CEEB) in an effort to establish an advanced-placement program for gifted students. The effect of this program (called the School and

The Origins of SMSG

College Study for Admission with Advanced Standing) was the reorganization of the high school mathematics curriculum for a few students. By completing a year of calculus in the senior year of high school and successfully passing an examination given by the CEEB, the student could be admitted with advanced standing to the participating colleges, sometimes with college credits for having completed the course in high school. This program, however, was admittedly designed for only a few highly talented students, and the resultant reorganization of the high school curriculum was simply a compression of the existing four-year program into three years in order to make way for the calculus in the final year.

The work that began in the 1950s was of a totally different nature.[2] As early as 1951, at the University of Illinois, the Colleges of Education, Engineering, and Liberal Arts established a Committee on School Mathematics (UICSM) to study problems associated with high school mathematics. Over the ensuing years, with financial support from the Carnegie Corporation and the U. S. Office of Education, the UICSM developed a sequence of entirely new mathematics courses for grades 9 through 12. These courses differed sharply from the traditional courses at the same grade levels in both content and approach. Under the ebullient leadership of Max Beberman, the UICSM produced, tested, and publicized a sequence of experimental textbooks and teacher's manuals that presented the mathematical world with a startlingly new and bold conception of the way they felt mathematics should be presented to high school students.

In 1955, the policy-making Committee on Examinations of the CEEB recommended to the Board that there be appointed

2. The 1950s are mentioned only because this is the decade when most of the work currently affecting the curriculum began. During the years 1930–40, the University of Chicago had developed remarkably modern mathematics offerings for lower-division courses, and there are other individuals and groups to whom some earlier attempts to modernize the curriculum could be traced.

a Commission on Mathematics. They suggested that the Commission be composed of distinguished high school and college mathematics teachers and research mathematicians. The task of the Commission would be to make a searching study of the "mathematics needs of today's American youth," and report its findings and recommendations to the Board. The members of the Committee were motivated by their experience with the advanced-placement program and the knowledge that some schools and colleges were already introducing curricula different from that the Board was testing. The Mathematics Examiners of the CEEB had developed a very natural concern that the curriculum they were testing (and had been testing and influencing for many years) might not be the most appropriate vehicle for meeting the mathematical needs of the times. The Board accepted the suggestion, and the Commission was appointed.[3]

After three years of intensive work under the chairmanship of A. W. Tucker of Princeton University, the Commission issued a monumental report of its findings and recommendations. The Commission found that much of the traditional curriculum was both necessary and desirable in the modern world, but other parts of it were useless vestiges of a bygone era. In addition, the Commission noted that the spirit in which mathematics was being taught in most high schools left a great deal to be desired in the understanding of mathematics being developed and in the attitudes toward mathematics being instilled in the minds of the students. The report, which was adopted by the Board and published in 1959, was characterized by a candor and specificity unusual in such a publication; further, it contained the forthright statement that the action of the Board in appointing the Commission constituted a frank attempt to influence the secondary school curriculum. Accompanying the report was a series of appendices, showing in detail the Commission's view of a satisfactory mathematics curriculum. In addition, the Commission caused to be written

3. See Appendix, List 1.

The Origins of SMSG

and published a sample textbook for the twelfth grade dealing with probability and statistics. The subsequent sales of this book gave testimony to the widespread interest created by the publication of the report.

Still other evidence of a shifting viewpoint toward high school mathematics was the work done by groups at Ball State Teachers College, University of Maryland, Southern Illinois University, and Boston College. The professional publications of the '50s abound in articles detailing classroom experiments and debating the psychological and philosophical implications of curriculum revision.

Additional impetus was given to the reform efforts when on October 4, 1957, the Soviet Union launched Sputnik I and injected the factors of national prestige and national security into the picture. This technological achievement raised questions regarding the mathematics curriculum in the United States that carried the controversy out of the world of scholars and into the public domain. The pressures on school administrators to "do something about mathematics" noticeably increased. In this climate of turmoil, debate, and public apprehension, the School Mathematics Study Group came into existence.

SMSG was organized by the mathematicians of the United States, and its genesis stems from two conferences, the second of which was the more important. During the '50s, both the Federal Government and the professional mathematical organizations evidenced increasing concern about the recruitment and training of mathematicians at the doctoral and post doctoral levels. The demand for manpower in this area had unquestionably exceeded the supply, and the gap was growing. Accordingly, on February 21, 1958, the National Science Foundation sponsored a conference of mathematicians in Chicago.[4] The purpose of the conference, called the Chicago Conference on Research Potential and Training, was to survey the problem of supply and demand with respect to research mathema-

4. See Appendix, List 2.

ticians. Despite the fact that the problem seemed to be one of graduate and post doctoral training only, it soon became apparent that participants at the conference felt otherwise. They took the view that concentrating effort on the training of mathematical personnel in the colleges at either the undergraduate or graduate level was a short-range attack on a long-range problem, and that one of the causes of the shortage of adequately trained persons was inadequate early schooling. The participants in the conference were aware of the efforts being made in many places to improve school mathematics, but they were also aware that most of these were local in scope and that they were being pursued under the auspices of single individuals or single institutions. In an attempt to widen the participation of the mathematical community in improving the teaching of mathematics at the lower levels, the conference adopted a resolution that, in effect, suggested that the American Mathematical Society (AMS) take official cognizance of the situation. The resolution requested that the President of the AMS, after consulting with the Presidents of the Mathematical Association of America (MAA) and the National Council of Teachers of Mathematics (NCTM), appoint a committee of mathematicians whose function it would be to "seek funds from suitable sources and proceed toward a solution of the problem," the problem being the existing state of the school mathematics curriculum.

Another meeting had already been scheduled for February 28, 1958, just one week after the Chicago Conference. This second meeting, called the Mathematics Meeting of the National Science Foundation, was held at the Massachusetts Institute of Technology in Cambridge and was presided over by Mina Rees of Hunter College, who had arranged it at the behest of a number of other mathematicians. Its announced purpose was to consider the existing mathematics curriculum in the schools of the United States. The location was chosen particularly to provide the participants with the opportunity to confer with the physicists who had, in 1956, founded the Phys-

The Origins of SMSG

ical Science Study Committee (PSSC) and who, at this time, had two years of very valuable experience in school-curriculum work. The members of the Cambridge Conference, as it came to be called, were chiefly research mathematicians, including the presidents of both the AMS and MAA, together with a number of members of the governing boards of both organizations.[5] After hearing from the physicists and a representative of the Commission on Mathematics, the conference engaged in a discussion that terminated in the reaffirmation of the AMS resolution enunciated in Chicago. The following day, March 1, 1958, the conference made specific recommendations as to tasks to which the AMS-appointed committee should address itself. These were: (1) to hold a four- or five-week writing session the next summer to prepare a detailed syllabus for a model secondary-mathematics curriculum beginning with the seventh grade, and (2) to arrange for the preparation and publication of monographs on topics in mathematics of interest and value to secondary school students. The conference further adopted, by unanimous agreement, a resolution designating a small subcommittee to act for the conference until such time as the President of the Society could appoint the suggested committee.[6]

The resolution adopted by the Cambridge Conference was extremely important. To appreciate how important, it is necessary to glance briefly at the nature of the American Mathematical Society. An organization composed entirely of mathematicians, it is the senior (in both age and sophistication of interests) of all of the professional organizations of mathematicians in the United States, and, consequently, it maintains just that degree of disinterest toward the ordinary affairs of mankind that it feels necessary to the protection of its chosen function, research in mathematics. Indeed, it was primarily for this reason that, in 1915, it aided and abetted the formation of the Mathematical Association of America, whose

5. See Appendix, List 3.
6. See Appendix, List 4.

function was to be that of serving the interests of the college teachers of mathematics so that the Society could concern itself with research. Following the establishment of the Association, the Society had felt itself free to ascend into the higher layers of the mathematical atmosphere, taking its membership with it, where, to all intents and purposes, it had remained.[7] Its membership included almost every mathematician of stature in the United States, and it was for this reason that the participants of both the Chicago and the Cambridge Conferences stipulated that the President of the Society should appoint the committee. They considered that the successful completion of the tasks of the committee called for the active participation of mathematicians of the highest caliber, and they knew that such participation would be much easier to obtain if the committee was created by the Society.

Still, there was the question of whether this was a proper concern of the Society. Therefore, in response to the desires expressed in the resolutions of the two conferences, Richard Brauer of Harvard University, President of the AMS, submitted a ballot (with arguments pro and con) to each member of the Council of the Society asking for an opinion on the propriety of making such an appointment in the name of the Society. The Council approved the idea of the appointment, and, on April 3, 1958, after conferring with the Presidents[8] of the MAA and NCTM, Professor Brauer named a committee of eight mathematicians[9] and charged them to act in accordance with the resolutions of the Chicago and Cambridge conferences.

It is difficult to overstate the importance of this move on the part of the Council and the President of the Society. For more than thirty years, the AMS had held itself aloof from the elementary and secondary school level of mathematics and had contributed very little to the teaching of it. With the ap-

---

7. There were exceptions to this generalization, but the number of such exceptions was not large enough to exert a detectable influence on the high school curriculum.

8. See Appendix, List 5.

9. See Appendix, List 6.

The Origins of SMSG

pointment of the Committee of Eight, it officially expressed an interest in the mathematics curriculum of the schools, and the approval of the Society made it possible for a large number of distinguished college teachers and research mathematicians to enter wholeheartedly into cooperation with high school teachers in a concerted effort to improve the quality and presentation of school mathematics. The Committee appointed by the President of the AMS was not a committee of the American Mathematical Society, and, in fact, had no connection with the Society other than through the act of appointment and through the fact that all of the mathematicians on the Committee were members. The Society, as such, could not be viewed as either approving or disapproving the work of the Committee, nor could the Committee in any way be deemed responsible to the Society, but many individual mathematicians who were members of the Society were to give much time and talent to help make the work of the Committee effective. The act of appointment gave clear indication that the long estrangement between research mathematicians and teachers of mathematics had been breached.

Yale University had early indicated a willingness to assume institutional leadership in the project, and Edward G. Begle, of the Department of Mathematics at Yale, was offered and accepted the responsibility of directing the work. Since one of the charges to the Committee by the Cambridge Conference had been to hold a four- or five-week summer writing session to produce a syllabus, and since the AMS appointment had not been made until April 3, much had to be accomplished in a very short time. The members of the Committee decided that the organization they were to establish would be called the School Mathematics Study Group, and it was in this name that the Group sought and promptly received an initial grant from the National Science Foundation in the amount of $100,000.[10] The grant was made on May 7, 1958, for the purpose of devising "a practical program which will improve the

---

10. Tentative approval of the project by NSF had been received on the final day of the Cambridge Conference.

general level of instruction in mathematics in elementary and secondary schools."

Nine days prior to the awarding of the grant, the Committee appointed by the President of the AMS convened at Hunter College in New York City for what proved to be its only formal meeting. The members gathered for the purpose of discussing the organization of SMSG. Several important decisions were made that shaped the administrative structure of the Group and that subsequently demonstrated a high degree of foresight.

It was agreed that the Director was to have the services of an advisory committee of approximately twenty-five persons. Some members of the Advisory Committee were to be college teachers of mathematics, some were to be high school teachers and supervisors of mathematics, and the remainder were to be representatives from the fields of engineering, the physical sciences, and school administration. It was to be the function of the Advisory Committee to consider general policy and to review continually the work of the Group. It was also decided that each activity undertaken by SMSG would be supervised by a panel, with membership drawn in part from the Advisory Committee, and that the work of each panel would be reviewed by the Committee as a whole. Finally, it was decided that an executive committee should be established consisting of five members chosen from the Advisory Committee. The Executive Committee was to meet regularly and often with the Director for the purposes of advising on policy. These three features of the organization—the Advisory Committee, the supervising panels, and the Executive Committee—existed from the outset and proved valuable and effective.

Immediately following the issuance of the grant on May 7, the Committee of Eight appointed twenty-six members to the Advisory Committee.[11] The membership was drawn from fourteen states with a geographical distribution ranging from Massachusetts to California and from Michigan to Louisiana. In-

11. See Appndix, List 7.

The Origins of SMSG

cluded were persons from colleges and high schools, both public and private, and from school districts of various types and sizes. Since it was the desire of the original Committee that SMSG cooperate in every way possible with existing experimental groups and that it lean heavily on their experiences, the Commission on Mathematics, the Curriculum Committee of the NCTM, and the UICSM were all represented on the Advisory Committee. Every effort was made to secure as wide a cross section of the nation's mathematical community as possible. At the time of the appointment of the Advisory Committee, five of the members also accepted appointments to the Executive Committee.[12]

Following the appointment of the Advisory Committee, Professor Begle found it necessary to concentrate almost entirely on preparations for the initial writing session that was to be held during the months of June and July. He had just one month to recruit personnel, establish an office staff, secure supplies, and make arrangements for the housing and feeding of the participants.

The most difficult problem was that of obtaining manpower for the writing session. It should be remembered that while the AMS launched SMSG, the launching was the end of the Society's responsibility, and it therefore was not possible (even had it been desirable) to seek its official assistance in the matter. Instead, Professor Begle set about the task on his own. He had the pooled knowledge of the members of the newly appointed Advisory Committee on which to rely, as well as a large number of personal contacts accumulated through his many years of active participation in the affairs of the AMS[13] and MAA. The results of his efforts surpassed all expectations. Despite the lateness of the hour, he was able to secure the services of forty-five persons.[14] Twenty-one of these were college teachers of mathematics, some of them chairmen of de-

---

12. See Appendix, List 8.
13. He had recently completed a six-year term as Secretary of the Society.
14. See Appendix, List 9.

partments of outstanding universities, some active in research, some of them experienced writers and all of them dedicated to the task at hand. Twenty-one high school teachers and supervisors also accepted the challenge the job offered. Among these teachers and supervisors were nationally recognized authorities in the field of mathematics education, authors of widely used commercial mathematics textbooks, and officers of local, state, and national professional organizations. Like the college mathematicians, each of them was wholeheartedly devoted to the objectives of SMSG. In addition to the high school and college representatives, the RAND Corporation, the Bell Telephone Laboratories, and the American Association for the Advancement of Science contributed participants.

Many of those attending the first writing session did so at great personal inconvenience; plans were canceled, calendars rearranged, long-anticipated vacations postponed, and, in some cases, important research projects regretfully laid aside. Some participants, unable to arrange their schedules in order to include full-time attendance, volunteered to devote such time as could be arranged. The manpower problem was, for the time being, well in hand.

The second problem Professor Begle faced was that of staffing an administrative office for the Group. He was fortunate in having available Mrs. Phyllis Stevens, an experienced and highly capable secretary, familiar with the sometimes curious ways of both college and school mathematics teachers, who was willing to cope with the ceaseless but necessary detail associated with the organization of a new project.

The problem of housing and feeding the participants and their dependents for this first writing session was solved by the Yale University administration, which made Trumbull College available. There was room enough in the college to house, feed, and provide working space for the entire Group.

2 First Writing Session

Yale was ready for the writing session, but were the participants of the writing session ready for each other? The whole future of the School Mathematics Study Group depended on the results of this first summer's work. If the Group was to succeed in its appointed task, it was essential that the mathematicians and the teachers establish a close working relationship. The relationship should be based on mutual regard, respect, and understanding; furthermore, each participant in each category should feel that his knowledge and experience were welcome and needed. In planning for the session, Professor Begle had tried to take advantage of every condition for fostering this feeling. Each participant had been informed that families were welcome. College and high school people were housed together, and all meals were to be taken in the college dining room. The culinary staff had been urged to outdo themselves in planning meals. Recreation facilities were provided for the participants and their families.

But all this forethought could have only an indirect influence in the establishment of the rapport that was necessary for a successful session; the essential ingredients were in the people themselves. To put it charitably, most of the participants were a few years removed from their college graduations. The last, and somewhat remote, contact most of the high school teachers had had with a research mathematician had been in their college years when the teachers had been students of college mathematicians. Consequently, some of the high school teachers were initially somewhat apprehensive about the correct protocol to observe in the new relationship. Curiously enough, the reverse relationship was true in some cases, the college mathematician's last contact with a high school teacher having occurred under similar circumstances, but, in this case, the mathematician had been the high school student. How does one deal with a Mr. Chips? Aside from the social aspects of the situation, some members of both groups were concerned about the intent of the other group. The high school teachers were apprehensive about the kind of mathematics the college teachers might propose for a new curriculum, and the college teachers were worried about the possibility that the high school teachers might resist any attempt to deviate very far from the status quo. As it developed, the misgivings of each group proved ill-founded.

The SMSG writing session of 1958 opened at Yale University in the commons of Trumbull College on June 23. Most of the invited participants were present. The first morning, those participants who had already worked on similar projects related their experiences. They reported on the methods of operation used by the writing teams of the Commission on Mathematics, the UICSM, and the University of Maryland Mathematics Project (UMMaP), and discussed the philosophy underlying the work of each. Also, at this opening session, Professor Begle explained the background of SMSG and elaborated on the philosophical and practical difficulties that lay ahead.

He pointed out that it was not to be the function of SMSG to attempt to establish a single curriculum for the schools of the United States. In the light of differences in individuals as well as differences in schools and regions, such a project would be undesirable even if it were possible. One of the things the Group *was* to do was to design a detailed outline for a series of textbooks in mathematics for grades 9 through 12, textbooks that could serve as a sample of what the Group con-

First Writing Session

sidered a curriculum suitable for a college-capable student of today. The reason for concentrating on college-capable students (roughly the upper third of the students at each grade level when ranked by grades, achievement, or ability, or some such index, admittedly a vague delineation) was that these students, with their college potential, were most in need of an improved mathematics curriculum. Furthermore, material prepared for such students could be of great value in showing teachers what new courses were to be proposed. It was clearly recognized, also, that any changes in the high school curriculum could be accomplished only with the wholehearted cooperation of classroom teachers, and every effort was to be made to give these teachers as much help and encouragement as possible. When completed, the sample textbooks for the better students could do much to afford such help, as could the commentaries for teachers that were to accompany the texts.

A second task for the group was to write a series of units on specific topics for students in grades 7 and 8. These units were to be of an experimental nature and would be tried out in the classroom during the academic year 1958–59; those that proved teachable would be considered as guides to the design of complete textbooks for these grades.

Because forty-five participants were involved in the writing session, it was felt that the most efficient way to proceed was in subgroups of eight or nine, each subgroup considering a specific level: one group for grades 7 and 8, and one each for grades 9, 10, 11, and 12. Each subgroup would consist of equal numbers of high school teachers or supervisors and mathematicians and would itself decide the manner in which it wished to operate. Five persons, three college and two high school teachers, were asked to serve as grade-level chairmen. Their function was to coordinate the work of the members of their respective subgroups and also to serve as intersubgroup coordinators to deal with such matters as articulation, terminology, and symbolism.

SMSG: The Making of a Curriculum

The specific task facing each subgroup was formidable indeed, and there could be no minimizing the responsibility that had to be assumed by each participant. This responsibility transcended questions of style, format, and approach; it arose from the very reason for the existence of SMSG. The overall purpose of the Group was the improvement of the teaching of mathematics in the schools of the United States. This subsumed, in particular, curricular considerations of the most fundamental kind. It was (and is) an acknowledged fact that the most important single factor in determining curricular content in the schools is the textbook. Individual teachers can and do use textbooks in widely varying ways and to greater or lesser degrees. On the level of practicality, however, particularly in the field of mathematics, the textbook determines almost exclusively *what* is taught and, to a large extent, *when* things are taught. If SMSG was to influence the mathematics curriculum in the United States, this influence would have to be exerted through the medium of sample textbooks. Therefore, the sample textbooks would have to contain the very best and most appropriate mathematics possible. Moreover, the books would have to exhibit a total curriculum that would be recognizably superior to that already in existence, and one that the teachers of this country would approve as a satisfactory replacement. The textbooks would have to be good enough to stimulate commercial publishing firms and individual textbook authors to produce new and improved books of a similar nature, because SMSG did not desire or intend to supply textbooks for the schools on other than experimental and short-term bases.

These were the facts that the participants in the writing session had to keep constantly in mind, and that in turn placed a heavy burden of responsibility on their efforts. SMSG was trying to influence the mathematics education of some millions of young people throughout the country, and this influence could be exerted only through a voluntary acceptance of the merit of the finished product. What had to be done, then, had to be done well.

First Writing Session

The subgroup concerned with the 7th and 8th grades, under the leadership of John Mayor of the American Association for the Advancement of Science, had a responsibility somewhat different from that of the other subgroups. This subgroup was not to write a syllabus for a course but a series of experimental units on single topics. Theirs was an area in which, it was generally agreed, much needed to be done. For a long time, the mathematics in the 7th and 8th grades had consisted of what many people considered a poorly organized presentation of much review of 5th and 6th grade arithmetic combined with some "functional" applications in the areas of taxes, household budgets, interest, and the like. These topics, while certainly of interest and importance to the citizenry of the country, were thought to be remote from the interests of 7th and 8th grade students and, even worse, to contribute very little to their understanding of the nature or uses of mathematics. If there was an area of the school curriculum that could be referred to as the doldrums of mathematics education, the 7th and 8th grades seemed to be the place. Little was known of what could be done with students at this level, because little had ever been tried. Some schools were offering algebra in the 8th grade, which simply meant that the students were covering the usual 7th and 8th grade material in one year. In view of the existing curriculum, such a feat was not particularly demanding. This sort of acceleration simply ignored the question of appropriate course content in mathematics for the junior high school student. Other schools were experimenting with what was called a "pre-algebra" course, which, in many cases, consisted of a very watered-down version of a few topics in algebra, generally in the area of operations involving negative numbers, and the solution of simple linear equations in one variable. In most cases, such experimentation could not be categorized as either inspired or effective.

The first task of the 7th and 8th grade subgroup was to do some exploratory work on feasibility. They were fortunate in having available the pioneering work of the UMMaP study of junior high school mathematics, which had been under way since September 1957 through a grant from the Carnegie Corporation and which was one of the few really serious attempts to create a new junior high school mathematics curriculum. UMMaP had not only developed some experimental material, but had already tried it out in actual classroom situations, and they generously made available to SMSG both their material and their experience. Indeed, Dr. Mayor, the chairman of the subgroup, was also the director of UMMaP.

As noted earlier, each of the subgroups devised its own working procedures, and these showed variations from one grade level to another. The 7th and 8th grade subgroup began its work by having each member examine the UMMaP material in detail. The members then met to decide what they themselves wished to do in the way of experimental units, with due regard for what had already been done by others. Through frequent contacts with members of the 9th grade subgroup, they were aware that the latter was to concern itself with beginning algebra. They decided, therefore, that, contrary to the approach taken by UMMaP, SMSG should refrain from including a heavy treatment of algebra in any of its 7th and 8th grade units and should, instead, concentrate on providing the students with experiences emphasizing logical patterns, mathematical vocabulary, and informal deduction and induction. They agreed further that, throughout each unit, the mathematical ideas developed would be associated with suitable applications, but that the applications would be secondary to the teaching of an understanding of the basic concepts.

In accord with the philosophical viewpoint that the junior high school curriculum is essentially of an exploratory nature, they decided that an informal study of geometry was also appropriate, together with a survey of the notions of measurement and approximation, elementary units on statistics and probability, and a unit on the mathematics of the lever. They found that they could borrow heavily from UMMaP in some areas.

To write the units, the subgroup divided itself into smaller

First Writing Session

teams of two, one high school teacher or supervisor and one mathematician. Choosing an area in which both members of the team were particularly interested, the writers began work. In general, the first step was to make a detailed outline of the unit. During this phase it was the task of the mathematician to determine those aspects of the topic that were of mathematical significance, whereas the classroom teacher, drawing upon a rich background of experience with the students to whom the material would be addressed, gave careful consideration to ways and means of presenting the material in the clearest fashion. This is not to imply that the mathematician did not make a contribution to method of presentation or that the classroom teacher made no contribution to sequence and content. While the primary responsibility for the mathematics lay with the mathematician and the primary responsibility for its teachability lay with the classroom teacher, each usually had something to contribute to the other. When an outline had been agreed upon, the actual writing began. In some cases the first draft was written by the mathematician and in others by the classroom teacher. The nature of certain topics made it possible for both members of the team to be writing simultaneously, each covering different aspects of the topic.

When a writing team was satisfied that it had an acceptable treatment of a topic, and this usually occurred at about the fourth or fifth draft, the material was duplicated and distributed to each member of the 7th and 8th grade subgroup. A general meeting of the subgroup was then convened and the material considered paragraph by paragraph. Almost invariably the meeting produced enough criticism, either of content, sequence, or motivation, to make it necessary for additional writing to be done. In most cases the rewriting was done by the authors of the first drafts, but if they felt they had done the best they could with the material, another team of writers would attempt to produce an acceptable version. Another meeting of the entire 7th and 8th grade group was then called to consider the new version. As soon as the group as a whole had

SMSG: *The Making of a Curriculum*

approved the treatment of one topic, another topic was attacked. By the end of the writing session, thirteen units had survived the intense critical screening and were considered ready for classroom testing. These units bore titles as follows:

1. What Mathematics Is and Why You Need to Know It
2. Numeration
3. Natural Numbers and Zero
4. Factoring and Primes
5. The Nonnegative Rational Numbers
6. Nonmetric Geometry
8. Informal Geometry I
9. Informal Geometry II
10. Measurement and Approximation
11. The Scientific Seesaw, or Mathematics at Work in Science
12. Uncle Sam as a Statistician
13. Chance
14. Mathematical Systems

An untitled unit, number 7, was proposed early in the session but, because of time pressure, was never completed. Unit 4A, entitled Supplementary Tests for Divisibility and Repeating Decimals, was completed and appended to Unit 4.

Meanwhile, the 9th, 10th, 11th, and 12th grade subgroups were preparing outlines for their respective grade levels. As a point of departure, they had the considerable amount of work that had been done by UICSM as well as the detailed recommendations of the Commission on Mathematics of the College Entrance Examination Board. They were not bound, however, to accept either the recommendations of the Commission or any of the work that had been done by UICSM, but were to put forward their own conception of a model course at each grade level. Each subgroup, therefore, had to grapple with problems of content, scope, sequence, and motivation. Above all, they had to come to an agreement on the point of view

First Writing Session

they hoped would permeate the textual presentation, that is, the spirit in which the material would be written.

It is difficult for persons not connected with the teaching of mathematics to appreciate the very great variety of ways in which any segment of mathematics can be viewed. It is widely believed that mathematics consists of a body of well-established facts that can be easily separated into self-evident units and fed to the student like coins to a savings bank. Nothing could be further from the truth. There are many ways in which any branch of mathematics can be viewed and, consequently, many ways in which it can be presented to students. Due to a combination of experience, personal philosophy, personality, and prejudice, each teacher or mathematician has his own notion of what constitutes a fitting and proper approach, and, of more particular consequence here, each has a strong conviction of just how each small topic ought to be handled in the classroom, how it ought to be related to the body proper of mathematics, and just where and when it should be presented to the student. Although a considerable overlap of these viewpoints exists among the members of such a group, there are many areas of disagreement. In the case of each subgroup of the SMSG writing team, these areas had to be clearly delineated before any serious attempt at writing could begin. The difficulty involved in coming to an agreement varied from subgroup to subgroup.

The 9th grade subgroup, with Henry Swain, Chairman of the Department of Mathematics of New Trier Township High School, Winnetka, Illinois, as its chairman, quickly arrived at an agreement with respect to content. They felt that it should be algebra. Algebra has traditionally been a part of the 9th grade curriculum, and neither the Commission nor UICSM had seen any reason for suggesting anything different. However, the more difficult questions of scope, sequence, and point of view remained, and these took longer to resolve. Almost three weeks of continuous day-long meetings proved necessary before a total sequence was approved. Part of the subgroup's

25

SMSG: The Making of a Curriculum

philosophy was that if a considerable degree of agreement on a matter could be reached before work began, the results of the work had a much better chance of being received favorably, and a great deal of rewriting and revising could be avoided.

Once a part of the sequence had been agreed upon, work began on detailed chapter outlines for this part. Again, before any detailed chapter outline was undertaken, substantial agreement was sought within the group as a whole concerning the scope and spirit of presentation. When such agreement was reached, individuals assumed responsibility for drafting a preliminary outline of the chapter or, in some cases, simply a section of the chapter. This work was done almost entirely at night or over weekends, because the regular working day was given over to the group meetings. These drafts were then duplicated and circulated to all of the members of the group for criticism. Following this, a second draft was written and criticized, and this writing and rewriting was continued until an outline resulted that was generally satisfactory to the group. Because of the lengthy pre-discussion, this process may not have been extended as far as proved necessary in certain of the other groups.

A detailed description, here, of the outline or of the philosophy underlying the 9th grade text would involve mathematical considerations beyond the scope of this work. To show the nature of the dialogue involved, however, it seems worthwhile to look at one of the more fundamental problems the group faced. Most persons who, at one time or another, have been exposed to a course in elementary algebra have little difficulty recalling that central to the subject is the use of letters of the alphabet as symbols. In particular, the letter x comes easily to mind. It is around the use of such symbols that some of the "modern" controversy centers. Traditionally, such symbols have been referred to as "unknowns," "literal numbers," "general numbers," and "variables," in some cases depending on context, in others depending on the whim of the user. The

First Writing Session

student has been told that these symbols are unknown numbers and that, in some cases, he can add these numbers ($x + x = 2x$) while, in other cases, he cannot (e.g., $x + y$). He has been instructed in ways of "finding the unknown," as, for example: if $x + 2 = 5$, then $x = 3$. But, on the other hand, he has been told that he is not to try to "find x" when writing such things as $x(x + 2) = x^2 + 2x$. This is due to the fact that the usual manipulations in which he becomes involved when working with such symbol groups produce $0 = 0$, which, though true, does not seem to tell him anything he wants to know about x. Worse, should he inadvertently apply his ingenuity to $x = x + 1$, he arrives at the mystifying $0 = 1$, which not only does not tell him anything about x, but causes him to call into question the sensibilities of anyone who finds interest in a discipline that deals with such absurdities.

It is one of the concerns of those seeking to revise the mathematics curriculum to make the meaning of such symbols clear to students, and to place their use on a sound logical foundation. Granting this, however, the best way to establish such a foundation is a matter of much controversy (hence, one reason for the lengthy discussions of the 9th grade subgroup). Present-day logicians, in their inquiries into the foundations of mathematics, have had occasion to use the notion of what they call a "placeholder," and it was this viewpoint that UICSM had adopted. Briefly: a number is an abstraction. Nobody has ever heard, felt, or seen a number, but the body proper of mathematics stems from the fact that the human mind can conceive of such abstractions. Furthermore, in discussing numbers, symbols are used which are called, in some cases, numerals, and in others, pronumerals, placeholders, or variables. The logicians, having found it necessary to work at varying levels of abstraction, have come to view a symbol such as "2" not as a number, nor even as the name of a number, but rather as a representation of the name of a number. Another representation of the same name of the same number is

SMSG: The Making of a Curriculum

"two." A number has infinitely many names; for example, another name for the number whose name can be represented by "2" is the name represented by the symbolism "1 + 1." A symbol such as "x," then, can be viewed as holding a place in an expression such as "$x + 5$" for a representation of a name of a number, hence the name "placeholder."

A step from the logicians are those who believe that the distinction between a name and its representation is unnecessary in all but the deepest discussions of foundations, and that it is sufficient to distinguish between the number itself and its name. Thus, the symbol "2" is the name of a number, just as the word "Tom" is the name of a person. At this level of abstraction, however, there are various ways of viewing symbols such as "x." In one view, when one is considering the expression "$x + 5$," the symbol "x" is conceived of as holding a place for the name of a number and is thus, conceptually, a "placeholder." In another view, the symbol "x" is used in the expression "$x + 5$" *as* the name of a number and is called a "variable." Inherent in both viewpoints, of course, is the agreement that there is some specified set of numbers with which the symbol "x" is associated.

Although there is almost universal agreement on the importance of distinguishing between a number and its name, the best way, mathematically, and pedagogically, to view the use of a symbol such as "x" is the center of much controversy. In view of the eminence of many proponents of each point of view, it would appear that, for the present, the way in which such symbols should be handled depends on the spirit in which the subject matter of algebra as a whole is handled, and this is chiefly a matter of who is doing the handling. It should be apparent, however, that the question is not a trivial one, since, in a sense, the way in which it is resolved determines to a greater or lesser extent the spirit in which the subject of algebra is taught. The question is essentially one of the "level of abstraction" and, barring gross misrepresentations, the argument reduces as much to a pedagogical matter as it does to a mathematical one. The problem of finding the level of ab-

First Writing Session

straction appropriate to the cognitive readiness of the student is a very real one, and the definitive answer, if such exists, has not yet been found.

To return to the matter at hand, the question of how to treat symbols was one (though not the only one) of the causes for the lengthy pre-discussions held by the 9th grade group before beginning detailed outlines of chapters, and their final decision was not free from critical attack by proponents of alternative viewpoints, as was to be expected.

The chairman of the 10th grade subgroup was Robert J. Walker, Chairman of the Mathematics Department of Cornell University. In accord with tradition and with the recommendations of the Commission on Mathematics of the CEEB, the group decided that the appropriate content of the 10th grade mathematics course was geometry. As was the case with the 9th grade subgroup, however, this decision was the easiest of the many they were called upon to make.

Geometry, as it is generally taught today, has been under attack by critics for some time. In fact, it seems safe to say that no aspect of the traditional high school curriculum has been criticized more severely, and for more diverse reasons. Before considering some of the criticisms, it should be recalled that high school geometry consists of a study of figures in planes and of solids in space. The study is conducted deductively. From a few undefined terms, some definitions, and some assumptions (called postulates), the student is shown (or is expected to show) how all the rest of geometry can be constructed by means of theorems. Theorems are statements of ineluctable logical consequences of the few underlying principles. The proofs of the theorems are usually displayed in a distinctive columnar arrangement, and are of a form referred to by mathematicians as "synthetic," so that the geometry studied is called a synthetic geometry. Furthermore, since it involves the use of a postulate to the effect that a point not on a line is contained in one and only one line parallel to the given line, it is called a Euclidean geometry.

The criticisms of the teaching of geometry in the high school fall largely into four categories. The first is concerned with certain faults of the postulate system and the absence of some required definitions. These faults are traceable to the treatment of the subject by Euclid. The second criticism has to do with the way in which Euclid's treatment has been condensed and modified for presentation to students. Thirdly, some critics question the appropriateness of a synthetic geometry in the school curriculum of the twentieth century. Finally, the way in which the subject is handled by teachers has been criticized. A brief examination of each of these types of criticisms may help to explain the decisions made by the 10th grade subgroup of SMSG.

Despite the claim by some that the geometry of Euclid is a good example of a rigorous deductive structure, it has long been known that when judged by the standards of modern mathematics, the structure exhibits critical logical shortcomings. One of these is the attempt made by Euclid to define every term. Instead of candidly recognizing the logical necessity for some undefined terms, Euclid attempted to ascribe properties to each term that would set it apart from everything else. This led to statements such as "a point is that which has no parts," which, unfortunately, does not categorize the notion of "point" in any meaningful way. Euclid's postulate system has also been shown to be defective. He used statements in certain of his arguments that could not be deduced from his formal assumptions. Commonly mentioned is the matter of "betweenness." His postulates provide no means for ordering the points on a line, and hence it is not possible to distinguish which of three points on a line lies between the other two. Other logical faults are present, but these suffice to illustrate what is meant by those who say that Euclid has been tried and found wanting in rigor.

The second class of criticisms pertains to the way geometry is presented in today's textbooks. It is asserted that the wording of definitions, axioms, postulates, and theorems has been so simplified that almost every concept involved is surrounded

First Writing Session

with a fuzzy aura of uncertainty, and that many statements occurring in today's books are downright erroneous. The preciseness of statement that characterizes mathematics (and that, indeed, is evident in much of the original Euclid) is almost completely absent. Note that these criticisms are entirely apart from questions of logical gaps in the structure. They tend to foster the reaction that if the foundations of the House of Euclid show some weakness, the logical structure being exhibited to modern American school children under the name of geometry is an absolute shambles.

The third type of criticism revolves around the question of whether synthetic geometry belongs in the school curriculum at all. Since the axiomatizing of algebra is strongly advocated, some persons feel that much of the reason for teaching synthetic geometry no longer exists. That is, to the extent that geometry is supposed to introduce the student to a logical structure, geometry itself can no longer be justified. With respect to the acquisition of facts about figures in a plane and about solids in space, all of the information required by the student can be imparted in much less time than a year.

The last category of criticism to be considered here concerns the manner in which geometry is being taught. It is said that the subject is usually presented with an extreme overemphasis on logical formalism as opposed to insight and creativity. The criticism is that the students spend far too much time trying to prove assertions made by somebody else and not nearly enough time making assertions of their own. It is claimed that many teachers will accept only one approved form for a proof and that students are thus not encouraged to develop any individual mathematical ingenuity. Furthermore, the role of intuition or independent reasoning is given little or no attention, and thus one very important phase of the subject is wholly neglected. Still another objection centers around the fact that plane and solid geometry have traditionally been taught as two separate and distinct courses. Some advocate that they be united in one course.

SMSG: The Making of a Curriculum

While the foregoing criticisms seem serious, it must not be inferred that they are without rebuttal. Classical synthetic geometry has never lacked for champions. With respect to the alleged defective postulate system, the reply is made that sufficient unto the day is the rigor thereof. Tenth grade children are not professional mathematicians and it is therefore extremely unrealistic to expect them to behave as such. With respect to the alleged debasing of Euclid, it has been pointed out that more students are able to learn more geometry now than ever before. It has been observed that the lengths resorted to by some mathematicians in wording statements so as to avoid all possible misinterpretation has resulted in circumlocutions so involved that the central idea of their pronouncements can hardly be found. As to the place of synthetic geometry in the curriculum, the point is made that without recourse to a highly elaborate and abstract approach, the subject of analytic geometry, so essential to the development of the calculus, depends heavily on synthetic geometry for its very existence. The fact that deductive methods are being introduced in algebra merely makes the teaching of deductive geometry easier, not less desirable. And lastly, the defenders feel that the geometry teachers should not be singled out as villains, there being enough bad teaching in other areas.

This then was the situation facing the 10th grade subgroup of SMSG, and their answer to the complex situation in the field of high school geometry was at once simple and bold. They would undertake the production of a new textbook in synthetic Euclidean geometry based on a system of postulates derived from a set formulated by G. D. Birkhoff of Harvard more than a quarter century ago. They felt that there was a place in the curriculum for synthetic geometry, and that a synthetic geometry could be presented that, while not logically unimpeachable, would still represent a distinct improvement over that currently in the schools both with respect to a sound postulational basis and to clear exposition. In line with the decisions of all other SMSG subgroups, they proposed to em-

First Writing Session

phasize accuracy of thought and language. They wanted their definitions and postulates precisely worded, while at the same time they planned to use a variety of intuitive and physical arguments as proper motivation. Furthermore, they hoped to be able to exploit the discovery process in a way that had not generally been done in geometry textbooks, and to provide the student with an opportunity to engage in the highly artistic and creative process of formulating theorems. Thus, what they hoped to do was ambitious in the extreme, and consisted of nothing less than trying to lay bare to the student the essence of mathematics, that curious interweaving of conjecture and certainty that characterizes the Queen of the Sciences.

As a result of this decision and because of the magnitude and difficulty of the task they had set themselves, this subgroup spent the entire writing session in continuous group meetings. The establishment of the postulate system and the hierarchy of theorems lay perforce in the province of the mathematicians, but even the results of this essentially mathematical task had to pass the test of teachability, and the high school teachers had to keep before the group the knowledge that the book was ultimately to go into the classroom. As one of the members of the group put it, "Each half of the group began its task with certain varieties of occupational naïveté, and our modus operandi was a long dialogue in which it was hoped that each half would whittle away the naïveté of the other."

By the end of the writing session, the long dialogue had produced a complete outline for a new geometry book. The subject matter would be synthetic Euclidean geometry, but with the addition of metric postulates (postulates explicitly establishing measures of line segments and angles), and would include a short treatment, near the end of the book, of analytic geometry. The outline also contained suggestions on the possible approach to each topic.

The 11th grade subgroup was led by Frank B. Allen, Chairman of the Mathematics Department of Lyons Township High

SMSG: The Making of a Curriculum

School and Junior College of La Grange, Illinois. The problems faced by this group were, in a sense, the same problems faced by the 9th grade group, because the 11th grade is traditionally devoted to a study of algebra. At this level, however, the situation is much more fluid than it is at the lower levels. Many schools offer only one semester of 11th grade algebra, whereas others offer two. In some school systems, trigonometry occupies the second semester of the 11th grade, while in others solid geometry is studied. The topics traditionally included in the 11th grade curriculum also vary from textbook to textbook. The 11th grade subgroup, therefore, had a much more serious problem with respect to scope than did those working at other grade levels. It was clearly impossible to include in one course all the material covered by all the textbooks currently used in second-year algebra. As a point of departure, the subgroup had before it the recommendations of the Commission on Mathematics. The Commission suggested for grade 11 a course called Intermediate Mathematics. The course was to consist largely of algebra, essentially the same algebra that is traditionally covered at this level. In addition, the Commission recommended that coordinate trigonometry and vectors be introduced to the students during the 11th year. They recommended that in the high school there be no separate course given over entirely to trigonometry. Trigonometry, like plane geometry, had, in the preceding years, been subjected to much criticism. Critics said that much of the time spent in the study of trigonometry was ill-spent and that the emphasis was being placed on entirely the wrong aspects of the subject. The criticism was made that instead of focusing attention on those parts of trigonometry of use and value in more advanced mathematics, an inordinate amount of time was being spent on computational trigonometry of a sort no longer useful either theoretically or practically. The Commission report itself is a case in point. In the Commission report, however, the criticism was only groundwork for the concrete proposals presented for a suitable course.

First Writing Session

As was the case with both the 9th and 10th grade groups, the 11th grade group spent much time in preliminary discussion. They had to agree on the viewpoint they wanted to adopt toward mathematics. They had to reach some agreement on the level of rigor they were to strive for, and above all they had to decide what to include and what not to include in their textbook. Despite the fact that the daylight hours of three whole weeks were given over to intensive group discussions, by the end of the writing session the 11th grade subgroup had written not only a syllabus for the year's work, but also a large number of sample chapters and sections (in more or less detail) illustrating the point of view they hoped would be adopted in the writing of the book. They had not, however, been able to solve their problems completely as was indicated by the fact that they entitled their final product a "syllabus" and not an "outline for a textbook." They specifically indicated on the first page of their report that it was possible that several sample textbooks could be extracted from the material as laid out.

The subgroup agreed that most of the textbooks generally available for 11th grade students were full of what might be called nonmathematics; they agreed that the books were by and large superficial and inaccurate expositions tending to conceal rather than reveal the structural character of the subject. Many texts that purported to feature a "meaningful approach" largely used rationalization in lieu of proof, and failed utterly to distinguish between facts to be assumed and facts to be proved. Such texts were described by one member of the group as "dreary collections of drill exercises, ideally designed to repel the able student, and useful only for the purpose of imparting specific manipulative skills by the intensive application of a large assortment of unrelated rules."

The treatment proposed by the 11th grade subgroup consisted of some algebra and some trigonometry, as the Commission on Mathematics had suggested. They wanted a book that would give the student some insight into the nature of mathematical thought as well as prepare him to perform certain manipulations with facility. They felt that at the 11th grade level the student was ready for more difficult ideas, and these they proposed to provide. At the same time, they wanted to use the student's intuition to as great a degree as possible so as to provide both motivation and a foundation on which to base the formal structure they proposed to erect. As was noted earlier, there was enough meat in the syllabus for a number of textbooks.

The chairman of the 12th grade subgroup was Donald E. Richmond, Chairman of the Mathematics Department of Williams College. In one sense this group had the easiest job of any of the subgroups. The 12th year of high school was traditionally given over to the study either of an additional semester of algebra or of trigonometry or of solid geometry, depending on the sequence adopted in the 11th year. In any event, all the mathematics normally included in the traditional high school program was being subsumed in the courses being planned for the 9th, 10th, and 11th grades. This left the 12th grade subgroup in the position of being able to choose such subject matter as they desired. The subject matter that came naturally to mind was the calculus. This engendered considerable discussion at the outset. It was generally recognized that in time calculus would probably become the standard course in the 12th grade. There was, however, a division of opinion on the extent to which such a course should be pushed at this time. The Commission had taken the position (which they asserted was the one held generally in the United States at the time) that calculus was a college-level subject. There were two reasons for so thinking. First, it seemed that most high schools in the United States lacked personnel qualified to teach college-level calculus, and, second, that the curriculum as it existed did not adequately prepare a student by the end of the 11th grade to undertake such a course. However, the Commission report did make the following assertion: "In the long run, improvements in the curriculum (beginning with the

First Writing Session

first grade) and in teachers' qualifications may eventually make it possible to move such a calculus course into the normal program for grade 12 of most schools." The 12th grade subgroup decided that since this feeling about the role of the calculus in the high school existed, and since there were reasonably satisfactory texts in calculus and analytic geometry already available, the subgroup could more profitably occupy its time in other areas. Once this crucial decision had been made, the group promptly decided to undertake the production of two textbooks. The first would be, in accordance with the recommendations of the Commission, a text on elementary functions for the first semester of the 12th year. The second text would be an introduction to modern algebra, that is, to "groups" and "fields." These decisions were all made within a day and a half after the participants started meeting as a group, and the remaining three and one-half weeks of the session were given over to the actual writing of text material.

Their working procedures were very similar to those adopted by the 7th and 8th grade subgroup. Teams of two were formed, and each of the teams took responsibility for one topic. Priority was given to the first textbook, *Elementary Functions,* and three teams of two were working on this particular book while one team of two devoted its attention to the book on modern algebra. By the end of the writing session, the 12th grade group had produced: (1) an elementary treatment of sets, relations, and functions, with exercises; (2) a chapter on exponential and logarithmic functions in fairly finished form; (3) a full outline of circular functions from the point of view of a winding function; and (4) a full outline for a course in modern algebra with typical examples and exercises.

Perhaps of greater interest than the activities of each of the individual subgroups was the emergence of the personality of the writing session as a whole. In the first few days of the session, the atmosphere was fraught with that air of diffidence and reserve normally associated with groups of strangers when they come together for the first time. There were, of course,

SMSG: The Making of a Curriculum

certain mitigating factors. Many of the college teachers had had occasion over the years to meet one another casually at professional meetings, and some of the high school teachers had worked together on committees for the National Council of Teachers of Mathematics and other such groups. Still, these meetings were of a totally different nature from the present one; also, many participants had never had occasion to meet any of the others. By the end of the first week, however, the atmosphere had undergone a profound and permanent change. The reasons for this are not hard to find. In the first place, Trumbull College, where the meeting was housed, is a small college, and no participant in the session lived more than 100 yards from any other participant. Furthermore, the rooms of the college were not equipped with private baths, and this necessitated some early discussions among the participants, their spouses, and allied members of the Group, relative to the apportionment of the existing facilities. Such discussions were difficult to conduct in a disinterested manner. Secondly, many of the members were in need of assistance from some of the others. When a mathematics teacher from a small high school in the Middle West has had his shirts ironed by the wife of the chairman of the mathematics department of a world-famous university, the relationship existing among them is altered irrevocably. The high school teacher, the wife, and the mathematician can never deal with each other again on quite the same level as before.

In addition, all participants ate in the same dining room, thus providing a maximum opportunity for families and individuals to get acquainted with each other. Coffee breaks were scheduled daily, one in the morning and one in the afternoon. These not only served to alleviate social tensions but, as it developed, provided indispensable opportunities for communication between members of different subgroups. When the foregoing circumstances were combined with the intense dedication of the participants to their common objectives, it was not strange that by the end of the first week the members of

First Writing Session

the group were working smoothly and with a high degree of efficiency.

Because the work being undertaken by the writing session was longitudinal in nature, it posed some rather formidable problems in matters of consistency and articulation. For example, it would clearly be undesirable for the 9th grade textbook to use a certain type of symbolism in one sense while the 11th grade used it in another, and, perhaps, the 12th in still another. Furthermore, the danger always existed that there would be basic philosophical disagreements among the treatments. The problem faced by the 9th grade group with respect to the point of view to take toward the meaning of "variable" is a case in point. If the 9th grade group, for example, made a decision in one way while the 11th grade group made a decision in another, the result could possibly lead to great confusion on the part of the students. Consistency in and of itself is not necessarily a desirable attribute in textbooks at different grade levels; still, certain types of inconsistencies are pedagogically more serious than others. If the style of writing in one textbook differs from the style of writing in another, or if the approach to a given topic is different from one year to another, the result is not necessarily bad; indeed, in the view of some, it might even be a virtue. However, if the language of the dialogue is shifted, or if the philosophical underpinnings are readjusted from one year to another, the results are apt to be more serious. The members of the various groups wanted to minimize inconsistencies of this type.

The articulation of the work of one group with that of another also raised problems. To the greatest extent possible, the writers wanted to avoid duplication of effort. Still, they recognized that when the finished textbooks were placed in the schools for trial, students using one of the textbooks might very well not have covered the material in the preceding book in the series. Consequently, certain of the ideas that were new —notably those dealing with sets—would need an introduction at whatever grade level they appeared. It was agreed that this sort of duplication could hardly be avoided at this stage. On the other hand, each subgroup wanted, if possible, to avoid exact duplication of topics that had been discussed at an earlier time. Though the notion of a spiral sequence of presentation is a well-founded one, such a presentation is difficult to design and increases in difficulty in direct proportion to the number of persons writing the sequence. Indeed, with many people concerned in the writing of a series of textbooks, there was danger that the spiral might degenerate into a circle and that the very same topic might be presented at two different grade levels in precisely the same manner. While these problems of consistency and articulation were not crucial at this stage of the planning, it was recognized that they would become crucial as soon as writing began on an intensive scale. As it developed, the morning and afternoon coffee sessions provided excellent opportunities for settling difficulties of this kind.

No specific working hours had been set for the participants in the session, but the groups soon established the habit of meeting from 8:30 in the morning until 5:00 in the afternoon. However, many of the groups found it necessary to continue meetings after dinner. Almost without exception, individual writers spent many hours both at night and during weekends either writing outlines or material of their own, or criticizing outlines or material of other members of their group.

Professor Begle established a temporary office near the entrance of Trumbull College, and, from this vantage point, guided and assisted the participants in their efforts. Having placed before the group on the opening day the overall purpose of SMSG and the specific duties of this writing session, he thereafter scrupulously refrained from participating in the deliberations of the subgroups and from any other activity that might in any way be interpreted as an attempt to influence their decisions. He made himself readily available to any member of the writing session who felt need of assistance of any kind. For reference, he had provided copies of many of the textbooks currently in use in the high schools, as well as col-

First Writing Session

lege textbooks in various categories. Samples of the experimental material of UICSM and UMMaP were made available and preliminary copies of the Report of the Commission on Mathematics were provided—the report itself was not to be made public for another six months. In addition to coping with a host of problems and arrangements for participants and their families, Professor Begle was also occupied with all of the routine paper work associated with the administration of a project of this type.

The writing session terminated on July 19 with a full meeting of all participants. During the course of this meeting the chairman of each subgroup reported on the activities and accomplishments of his group. Each report was followed by a brief discussion. In view of the close intermingling of the personnel of all the subgroups at the coffee breaks and at mealtimes, very little of the work of one group was not known to all members of the other groups; consequently, the discussions following the reports were not lengthy. Dissenting opinions had already been registered and reregistered many times. By noon, the group had heard a summary of what it had accomplished. The 7th and 8th grade subgroup had produced thirteen experimental units with exercises. The 9th grade subgroup had produced a detailed outline for an algebra textbook complete with examples of the sort of mathematics they expected to be included in the textbook, together with the reasons why they had chosen, at each point, to do what they did. The 10th grade subgroup had formulated a set of postulates for a geometry textbook and had then completed an outline for the entire book. The 11th grade subgroup had compiled a syllabus covering the mathematics it recommended for the 11th grade, and a considerable amount of writing had been finished. Several chapters were complete and fragments of additional chapters had been written, all illustrating the sort of mathematics that the writers hoped would be included in the 11th grade book. The 12th grade subgroup, having chosen to follow the outline proposed by the Commission on Mathe-

SMSG: The Making of a Curriculum

matics for the first-semester course, had completed preliminary drafts on three chapters of the book and, at the same time, had completed an outline for a one-semester course in modern algebra. All in all, the results were impressive.

The group concluded the summer's work by adopting two resolutions which they urged Professor Begle to disseminate widely. One resolution asked school districts to remove the restriction, if present, that an adopted textbook remain in use for a period of from three to six years. The participants felt that such a restriction tended to freeze the mathematics offerings of a district longer than was healthy. The second resolution adopted by the group advocated that students, whenever possible, be permitted to retain their mathematics textbooks for their personal libraries, and that if necessary paperbacked textbooks be sought by school authorities. The group felt that the ownership of textbooks could prove very valuable to the student in later school years.

When the final session of the final day was adjourned and the participants began their long journeys toward the four corners of the United States, SMSG had demonstrated something of far greater importance than any amount of written material or any number of resolutions. This was the certain knowledge that it was possible for college mathematicians and high school teachers of mathematics to work together cooperatively in a vigorous and effective manner. Like most other human relationships within a group, the precise nature of the relationship developed within the group at Yale is difficult to describe. It consisted of the interactions of a large number of different personalities taking on something of the nature of any one of them and yet, in the total, transcending the sum of all of them. At the outset of the writing sessions, the group discussions were punctuated with "Professor," "Doctor," "Mr.," and "Mrs.," and were conducted with that air of studied politeness commonly associated with conversations in which each party is striving desperately to avoid offending the other. Within a very short time and with very few exceptions, the

First Writing Session

first name was the accepted form of address. Although the conversations continued to be conducted with all politeness, the formal punctillio which marked the earlier meetings was no longer in evidence. In fact, in less than a week, the members of the subgroups had established relationships sufficiently sound and friendly to permit argument.

In most groups it was soon found that when differences of opinion arose, it was better to keep talking and bringing out pertinent ideas until there was general agreement instead of voting on the issue prematurely. This had the beneficial effect of making everyone feel that his opinion was important and valued, as well as preventing the formation of factions or schisms within the subgroup. Some conversations produced as much heat as they did light, but in no cases were differences of opinion placed on a personal basis, nor was there ever any occasion to question the motives from which arguments sprang. This is attributable in no small part to the realization by the participants that they were engaged in an extremely serious venture, one that called for the highest degree of selflessness. The attitude of mutual esteem and respect that the participants in the Yale session came to have for one another was to prove of the very highest importance in the work that lay ahead.

3 First Year

When engineers set about building a new machine of some kind, they frequently construct a model first. If the model does not display the properties they expect of the finished product, they may decide that the project is not feasible, or they may revise their original plans to compensate for difficulties uncovered by the model. In either event they learn something, and they save, over the long run, a very great deal of time, effort, and money. The first writing session at Yale can be compared to a model that demonstrated that the collaboration of research mathematicians and high school teachers was possible. The School Mathematics Study Group now felt it worthwhile to proceed with the project of writing a set of sample textbooks, although there was still much to be done before the writing could begin.

SMSG had been organized very hastily in order to prepare for the writing session at Yale, and could not honestly be said to exist yet as an organization. The headquarters staff consisted of Professor Begle and his secretary, operating from a small room in Leet Oliver Hall at Yale that was never intended to serve as a headquarters for a nationwide enterprise. Furthermore, they were confronted with matters needing immediate attention. They had the material produced by the writing sessions, which had to be organized and reproduced for distribution. The units written by the 7th and 8th grade sub-

First Year

group had to be reproduced in quantity and delivered to the schools chosen to experiment with the material in the classroom. The stipends for the participants at the writing session had to be calculated and sent to the Bursar's Office of Yale for payment. There were, of course, other matters needing attention, but these few had to be accomplished very rapidly.

The pilot grant of $100,000 that Yale had received in May 1958, though made for the calendar year, had specifically been awarded for just three items: primarily for the cost of the writing session, but also for defraying headquarter expenses and for expenses involved in preliminary meetings and conferences. In accordance with an understanding reached at the time of the original grant, Yale University, as soon as the success of the writing session was apparent, made application to the National Science Foundation for additional funds to carry on the work. On September 29, 1958, an extension of the grant was made to Yale in the amount of $1,200,000, to run until September 1, 1959, which included funds for a session to be held in the summer of 1959 for the purpose of writing the textbooks that had been outlined during the summer of 1958. It was understood that Professor Begle would be willing to continue as Director of the Group, and Yale University had agreed to give him a year's leave of absence from his university responsibilities so that he could devote full attention to the advancement of the project.

Within two weeks of the close of the writing session in July 1958, SMSG headquarters at Yale had moved from Leet Oliver Hall to Henry Barnard Hall, first into two large rooms and subsequently into four. An additional full-time secretary was obtained, and numerous part-time assistants, most of them typists, were put to work preparing the 7th and 8th grade units for reproduction. The only piece of permanent equipment obtained prior to the writing session had been a copying machine, and it was necessary now to procure additional items such as typewriters, filing cabinets, dictating equipment, and the usual office furniture. In January 1959, a third full-

SMSG: The Making of a Curriculum

time office worker was hired for the headquarters staff.

With the close of the writing session, the arrangements for the tryouts of the 7th and 8th grade experimental units were of pressing importance, and some decisions had to be made about procedures to be used. The original NSF grant had stipulated that one of the specific tasks of SMSG was "to prepare, try in selected schools, and revise sample textbooks," and the trial and revision aspects were, from the beginning, felt to be of the utmost importance. It was one thing to write and criticize material as an authority, but the real test would come in the classroom. The trial of the material was as important to the work of SMSG as the writing itself. The educational landscape was strewn with the bleached bones of "authorities" who had made the mistake of substituting opinion for fact, and SMSG was determined not to make the same mistake.

It was decided that the most efficient administrative procedure to adopt for testing was to establish centers. A center was a city or locality in which tryouts were to be held, and was under the supervision of a local person designated as chairman. The chairman of a center was responsible for the procurement of suitable teachers and classes for the tryout process. He was also charged with the responsibility of distributing all material to the respective teachers and of returning the detailed criticisms from each teacher to SMSG headquarters. Assigned to each center was a consultant. The consultant was a college mathematician whose task it was to meet periodically with the teachers of the experimental classes and to help them in any way possible do a better job of teaching the material. This help usually took the form of supplying background information with respect to the mathematical concepts involved in the written material and of answering any questions the teachers (or their students) had about the mathematics.

The "center" concept for experimental testing of material proved highly successful, and was the plan SMSG was thereafter to use in all such work. It had many advantages. By de-

First Year

centralizing the details of distribution, a considerable amount of time and effort was saved at headquarters. Furthermore, by having a local person in charge, each of the very wide variety of school systems used in the testing was dealing with a person who was familiar with the local customs and procedures, and who was generally able to cope with minor emergencies and crises on the spot. The center chairmen were selected with great care and were persons highly regarded in the areas in which they were working. All the teachers using the experimental materials were volunteers willing to try the materials. The mathematical consultants used by the centers were persons acceptable both to the local school district and to SMSG. All material for tryout was supplied to the school district by SMSG, and at the end of the experiment became the property of the student. Teachers who participated in the experiment were paid by SMSG for the time (usually two days a month) they had to spend in meetings and in preparation over and above their normal school day. The consultants also were paid by SMSG, so that there was no financial outlay by the school district. Though the centers were geographically widespread, their selection was restricted somewhat by the necessity of having a consultant readily available. This meant that they had to be located in the vicinity of a college or university.[1]

Each center tried out as much material as it could. To get as many units tested as possible, specific units were assigned to particular centers. Some units were tried out in all centers, and all units were tried out in some centers. Following the completion of a unit, the teacher was requested to fill out a questionnaire which provided for much specific information about the material itself, its teachability, and the reactions of both the teacher and the pupils to its use. These questionnaires were channeled through the center chairmen to SMSG for use at the writing session to be held the following summer.

Before the trial program was fairly under way, SMSG decided that one very valuable means of ensuring that the trials

1. See Appendix, List 10.

be conducted under the best conditions (and this was deemed essential) would be to hold an orientation conference for the classroom teachers who would be using the material. At this conference, to be paid for by SMSG, the teachers could meet some of the writers, and could become acquainted with the thinking behind each of the units they were to be teaching. In this way, the teaching could be conducted with full knowledge of what was being sought and, perhaps more important, with the realization that SMSG was a team effort and that they were important members of the team.

Accordingly, SMSG made arrangements to hold a conference in Washington, D.C., on November 21 and 22, 1958. The participants at the conference included most of the classroom teachers involved in the SMSG tryout, the panel on 7th and 8th grades of the School Mathematics Study Group (which included some of the writers of the material), and some teachers who possessed some experience in teaching substantially similar material in the Maryland Study. By the time the conference adjourned, the teachers from the centers not only had been familiarized with the material they were to teach and with its underlying philosophy, but they had been given valuable teaching suggestions by experienced teachers.[2] It was made clear to them that the responsibility for determining the classroom effectiveness of the material lay in their hands, and that without their enthusiastic cooperation it would not be possible to get a meaningful evaluation of the writers' efforts.

The panel on 7th and 8th grades,[3] whose members attended the conference, had been appointed by the newly organized Advisory Committee of SMSG. It will be recalled that when SMSG was being formed by the Committee of Eight, provision was made for the existence of an advisory committee of twenty-six members. The Advisory Committee held its first formal meeting on July 5, 1958, at Yale. Sixteen of the committee members were present, and during the course of the meeting

2. See Appendix, List 11.
3. See Appendix, List 12.

First Year

they formulated a set of objectives for SMSG which are perhaps best presented by *SMSG Newsletter* no. 1:

> The world of today demands more mathematical knowledge on the part of more people than the world of yesterday, and the world of tomorrow will make still greater demands. Our society leans more and more heavily on science and technology. The number of our citizens skilled in mathematics must be greatly increased; an understanding of the role of mathematics in our society is now a prerequisite for intelligent citizenship. Since no one can predict with certainty his future profession, much less foretell which mathematical skills will be required in the future by a given profession, it is important that mathematics be so taught that students will be able in later life to learn the new mathematical skills which the future will surely demand of many of them.
>
> To achieve this objective in the teaching of school mathematics three things are required. First, we need an improved curriculum which will offer students not only the basic mathematical skills but also a deeper understanding of the basic concepts and structure of mathematics. Second, mathematics programs must attract and train more of those students who are capable of studying mathematics with profit. Finally, all help possible must be provided for teachers who are preparing themselves to teach these challenging and interesting courses.
>
> Each project undertaken by the School Mathematics Study Group is concerned with one or more of these three needs.

It was the function of a panel to supervise the work undertaken in each project. By the end of August 1958, members had been appointed to four panels, one on the 7th and 8th grades, one on sample textbooks, one on monographs, and one on teacher training materials. The work of each of these panels merits discussion.

The panel on 7th and 8th grades had the responsibility of supervising all of the writing and testing of classroom materials at these grade levels. Their first meeting was held in Washington, D.C., in September 1958, and the major portion of the three days the panel met was devoted to editing the 7th and 8th grade units that had been produced at the Yale writing session. Three additional meetings of the panel were held during the academic year 1958–59; another meeting in Washington, D.C., in November at the time of the orientation conference for the experimental teachers; a meeting in Dallas, Texas, on April 2 and 3; and a meeting in Dearborn, Michigan, in June, prior to the start of the second writing session. The purpose of all these meetings was to keep abreast of the interim writing that was in progress at each of the centers (new units were in the making) and to organize an outline for a 7th grade textbook that could be submitted for the consideration of the participants in the writing session to be held in the summer of 1959. The last meeting, held in Dearborn, also laid detailed plans for conducting the writing session.

The panel on sample textbooks[4] was responsible for supervising the writing of the textbooks for grades 9 through 12, and included in its membership the chairman of each of the subgroups formed at Yale. The panel held its first meeting on October 11, 1958, in New York City, and its second on January 17, 1959, also in New York City. Its chief concern during this period was the establishment of working plans, coordinating interim writing, and helping with the recruitment of writers for the coming summer writing session.

The panel on monographs[5] had been one of the earliest panels appointed by the Director and had been hard at work even prior to the Yale writing session. One of the original

4. See Appendix, List 13.
5. See Appendix, List 14.

First Year

projects of SMSG was the production of a series of short expository monographs on various mathematical subjects that were to be written by outstanding mathematicians. The purpose of the monographs was to disseminate good mathematics at the secondary level, mathematics that would serve to supplement curricular offerings, arouse the interest of gifted students, and, in general, present the subject as a satisfying, meaningful human activity. This panel, unlike the others, was composed chiefly of college mathematicians, although two of the thirteen members were high school teachers. The reason for the imbalance (if it may be so referred to) was that one of the primary tasks of the panel during its early existence was the recruitment of writers of stature, and it was felt that this could probably be done more effectively by college people.

The Physical Science Study Committee at MIT was already engaged in the production of monographs on physics, and provided valuable advice to the mathematicians. The panel on monographs decided that although the physicists had placed their monographs in the hands of commercial editors for production purposes the mathematical monographs should be produced in a different way. Therefore, the panel appointed an editorial committee of mathematicians whose job it was to perform this function. (The mathematical community was still recovering from the unfortunate efforts of a zealous editor who had sought to smooth the prose in the final version of the Report of the Commission on Mathematics by changing all references to "real numbers" in the report to the more elegant "genuine numbers"!) By November, the editorial committee of the panel was negotiating with nine authors who had submitted outlines or sample chapters, and with several others who had agreed to write monographs. By June of 1959, the committee had complete first drafts of several monographs and the New Mathematical Library (as it was to be called) was well under way.

The panel on teacher training[6] was to devote its attention

6. See Appendix, List 15.

SMSG: The Making of a Curriculum

to the production of textbooks, study guides, and other materials for teachers who wished additional training in mathematics. The pre-service training of teachers was considered properly a concern of the Committee on the Undergraduate Program (CUPM) of the Mathematical Association of America, and SMSG was interested only in in-service training. There was clearly a need for some kind of help for teachers. The number of mathematics teachers in the secondary schools of the United States who were poorly prepared to teach mathematics was staggering. It was estimated by some to be more than half of all mathematics teachers. Over 25 per cent of them had never completed a course in the calculus. Many had been pressed into the field from other subject-matter areas to help cope with the problem of an increasing number of students and a decreasing number of qualified teachers. It was fruitless to discuss a revitalization of the curriculum without, at the same time, considering ways and means of providing badly needed assistance to the corps of high school mathematics teachers.

But how could such help be provided? There were a number of possibilities. The National Science Foundation had, since 1953, been providing very valuable aid in this area by sponsoring summer and academic-year institutes for high school mathematics teachers in various universities and colleges. Teachers attending these institutes were paid for attending, and all tuition and fees to the institutions offering such institutes were also paid by NSF. Despite the steady growth in the number of institutes offered, they could involve only a very small percentage of the nation's high school mathematics teachers. Furthermore, the institutes frequently did not have materials available appropriate to the needs of the teachers attending. Local in-service training was another possibility, but it was very difficult to find effective ways to provide it. Teaching is a demanding profession, as anyone who has ever engaged in it knows. Five or six hours a day in front of a class is an exhausting stint, and when extracurricular activities, supervision, and

First Year

the marking of stacks of papers are added to this, the teacher has little time or energy left to give to the task of learning more mathematics. That many of them, in spite of crushing schedules, do undertake night classes or attend local workshops is an indication of the dedication with which they practice their profession.

The panel on teacher training of SMSG was fully aware of the nature and the magnitude of the problem of retraining mathematics teachers. After surveying what was already being done, the panel felt that material suitable for use in summer and in-service institutes was badly needed and proposed to devote particular attention to this. By March of 1959, they had sponsored the publication of the first of a series of Studies in Mathematics, a volume by R. D. Luce of Harvard University, entitled *Some Basic Mathematical Concepts*. This study was an exposition of elementary set theory with applications of set concepts to various parts of mathematics. In addition, SMSG was already supplying free of charge a *Study Guide in Modern Algebra,* which provided a concise list of references to books of value to high school teachers. In June 1959, a second volume of Studies in Mathematics was released in a preliminary edition. This volume was written by C. W. Curtis, of the University of Wisconsin, Paul H. Daus, of the University of California, Los Angeles, and Robert J. Walker, of Cornell University and dealt with Euclidean geometry based on ruler and protractor axioms. It offered an excellent source of background information for teachers who proposed to teach the SMSG geometry book outlined at Yale. The panel on teacher training met only once during the 1958–59 academic year. The meeting was held in Dallas, Texas, on April 4, 1959, and dealt with plans for future publications.

In addition to coordinating and assisting the efforts of the four panels to get under way, Professor Begle and the headquarters staff of SMSG had other administrative concerns. Plans had to be made for the second writing session. Some means had to be devised to keep the public informed of the

53

SMSG: The Making of a Curriculum

activities of SMSG, because inquiries were reaching the office in a steadily widening stream. Closely associated with the problems of curriculum in the schools was a whole complex of involved questions relating to the learning of mathematics, questions whose answers demanded the assistance of psychologists of the highest caliber. Some exploratory work was needed in this area. The question of extending the work of SMSG to the elementary level was one that needed the advice of a large number of persons concerned with that level and who were not yet associated with the group. The mathematical needs of the non-college-bound student had to be considered by the Advisory Committee and the committee's recommendations in this regard implemented. Interim work was under way at most grade levels, and this had to be monitored. The flow of material to and from the 7th and 8th grade experimental centers had to be maintained. In short, the problem of trying to set up an efficient administrative organization for SMSG was complicated by the fact that its obligations were steadily increasing.

The experimental centers were in full operation by December 1958. The duplication of the units for grades 7 and 8 had been placed in the hands of the Yale Clerical Bureau, which, after mimeographing the material, returned it to SMSG headquarters in bundles of loose sheets. Many hours of work by part-time help were necessary to sort and arrange these sheets and to pack and ship them to the centers. Completed questionnaires were flowing in from the centers, and these had to be catalogued and their contents digested for use during the coming summer. Despite the acquisition of additional office space, cardboard boxes had to be temporarily pressed into service as filing cabinets, and the storage problem, while under control at the moment, gave promise of becoming serious as the activities of SMSG expanded.

Some interim work was being attempted at all levels. The writing of new 7th and 8th grade experimental units at the centers has already been mentioned. The 9th grade subgroup

First Year

had small teams in Minnesota and Connecticut working on textual material. E. E. Moise, then at the University of Michigan, arranged for a leave of absence during the spring semester of 1959 and undertook to write a first draft of the 10th grade geometry textbook following the outline laid down at the Yale writing session. The 11th grade subgroup, it will be recalled, had a serious problem with respect to the scope of their course, and as a result no heavy interim work could be done. The situation was so serious that a special meeting of this subgroup was held in Chicago on February 28, 1959, to try to thresh out an outline acceptable to all, and to solve problems of duplication that existed between their proposed material and that of the 12th grade subgroup. The chairman of the 11th grade subgroup had already formulated a tentative outline for a text, and by the time the meeting adjourned, this outline had been approved by the other members and specific working assignments had been made for the next summer's writing. Unfortunately, the members of the subgroup were unable to find time in their universally crowded schedules to do much individual writing prior to summer. The 12th grade group had some members working on revised drafts of the material produced at Yale, as well as having in preparation two new outlines for textbooks for the second semester. One of these outlines was for an alternative course in groups and fields (modern algebra) and the other for an intuitive approach to the calculus.

An enormous amount of correspondence between the chairmen of the groups, the writers, and Professor Begle was necessary to coordinate this effort and lead to production of useful material. The group chairmen acted as liaison between headquarters and the writers, and most of the correspondence was channeled through these people. As they received material from the writers, they forwarded it, together with their comments, to Professor Begle at Yale.

The Advisory Committee of SMSG met only once during the academic year, on January 24, 1959, in Philadelphia, but they conducted a great deal of business by mail. Among their concerns during the period was the extension of the work of SMSG into the elementary grades and into the area of mathematics for non-college-bound students. The Advisory Committee suggested that the latter area was of sufficient concern to warrant the appointment of a panel for the purpose of supervising some sample textbooks directed toward this segment of the population. The writing of such texts, however, could not reasonably be expected to start in 1959.

The elementary school problem was of a different nature. It encompassed an area outside the grade levels with which SMSG was currently working, and the Advisory Committee felt that the advice of a wider representation of the mathematical community would be valuable. To obtain the necessary advice, SMSG sponsored a conference on elementary school mathematics. The conference was held in Chicago on February 13–14, 1959, and was attended by 56 persons prominent in the fields of mathematics and mathematics education.[7]

It developed that the participants were unanimously agreed that a comprehensive study should be made of mathematics in all grades from kindergarten through grade 12. They adopted a resolution requesting the Director of SMSG to appoint an ad hoc Committee on Elementary School Mathematics to recommend appropriate action to implement the study. The recommendations were to be made to the Advisory Committee of SMSG, which might thereafter take such action as it deemed necessary and proper. As a result of the conference and the subsequent report of the ad hoc committee appointed by Professor Begle, the Advisory Committee recommended the appointment of a panel on elementary school mathematics. But again, because of the exigencies of prior activities, the work of this panel could not be gotten under way in 1959. One of the recommendations of the ad hoc committee was that psychological studies be made in the area of the learning of mathematics, and, although no formal action was taken at the time, the Advisory Committee of SMSG was aware that much

7. See Appendix, List 16.

First Year

valuable work could be undertaken in this area when time and circumstances permitted.

It was during the academic year 1958–59, also, that some lines of communication had to be established between SMSG and the classroom teachers of the country, as well as the general public. There had been little publicity upon the formation of SMSG or upon the initial writing session at Yale. This was largely by design, since the atmosphere at the time was charged with tension following the recent successes of the Soviet rocket engineers. Because SMSG sprang from roots running much farther back in time, and because it seemed desirable to avoid even the semblance of opportunism, publicity was held to an absolute minimum. On the other hand, it must not be inferred that SMSG was being shrouded in secrecy, or that it was conducting its activities without the full knowledge and consent of the professional organizations devoted to mathematics and mathematics education. It will be remembered that many of the top officers in these professional organizations were either members of the Advisory Committee or writers for SMSG, and, indeed, the presidents of the AMS, MAA, and NCTM aided in the establishment of the group. The situation was that SMSG was beginning its activities in somewhat emotionally charged times, and it believed that, because the task it faced was not of a transient nature, its work deserved to be launched in as thoughtful and serious a climate as possible.

It became appropriate, however, as soon as its work was well under way, for SMSG to acquaint interested persons with its nature and purposes, and to this end it began the publication of a series of newsletters. The first of these appeared in March 1959 and was mailed to all members of the NCTM. It contained a brief explanation of the history of the formation of SMSG, together with a statement of its objectives and operations. The names of the members of the Advisory Committee, those of the members of each panel, and those of the participants in the 1958 writing session were included. It also contained a statement about the projected activities of the group, and invited any person who desired to keep informed of its activities to join those on the newsletter mailing list.

Other avenues were employed to disseminate information about SMSG. Representatives of the group appeared on the programs of virtually all the local, regional, and national conferences held by the MAA and NCTM during the academic year 1958–59. Many teachers' institutes across the country devoted time to discussions of the work in progress. The pages of the professional journals carried articles devoted to the group and its work. In short, the activities of SMSG were being brought to the attention of a wider and wider audience.

As the summer of 1959 approached, final arrangements had to be made for the second writing session of SMSG. Because SMSG did not want the albatross of sectionalism draped around its activities, it had been decided to hold writing sessions at two widely separated locations during the months of June, July, and August 1959, and neither was to be at Yale. The 7th and 8th grade group was to hold an eight-week writing session at the University of Michigan. Beginning a week after the opening of this session, the remainder of the writers would open a nine-week attack on the 9th, 10th, 11th, and 12th grade texts at the University of Colorado. Early in 1959, Professor Begle made arrangements to secure the services of John Wagner, of the University of Texas, on a full-time basis for the academic year 1959–60. Mr. Wagner would serve in the capacity of Assistant to the Director of SMSG, and his first responsibility would be to cope with all problems arising in connection with the University of Michigan writing session during its term of existence, and to remain in Ann Arbor for the entire session as Professor Begle's representative.

Professor Begle had as a nucleus for writers at both sessions almost all of those who had attended the Yale writing session in 1958. But many more were needed. Throughout the period from July 1958 to June 1959, Professor Begle was combing the United States for talent. It seemed important that every

First Year

section of the country be represented in the work, and that the very best people possible be recruited. Furthermore, as many branches of mathematics as possible should contribute mathematicians to the effort, and a great diversity of sizes and types of high schools should have experienced teachers to represent them.

In addition to writers, skilled and experienced mathematical typists had to be found, because the work to be done had to be reproduced quickly and accurately, and called for a high order of typing ability. Typewriters with special mathematical keyboards were necessary if laborious hand lettering was to be avoided. The services of professional draftsmen had to be secured to produce the large number of graphs and charts that would be involved in the texts. Since more than outlines would be forthcoming at this session, duplicating machines were also needed.

The textbooks to be written during the 1959 sessions were to be tested in the classroom during the 1959-60 academic year. This presented difficult problems in the printing of the texts. While the 7th and 8th grade experimental units had been duplicated by the Yale Clerical Bureau, and the newsletters had been printed by the Printing-Office of the Yale University Press, the numbers of copies of sample textbooks and the speed with which they had to be produced made it necessary to seek other agencies for the job. An agreement was made with commercial printers for the massive job of producing the preliminary editions for use in the tryouts. The printing would be done by a photo-offset process from master copy supplied by SMSG. In order to have the first volume ready for use in September, rigid deadlines had to be established for production of finished copy, and, as will be seen, these deadlines had an effect upon the operations of the writing session.

Then, of course, there was the problem of setting up experimental centers. The number involved in the 1959-60 tryouts would be much larger than the few who were involved with the 7th and 8th grade tryouts, and the flow of material would

SMSG: The Making of a Curriculum

be of an altogether different order of magnitude. Planning for centers began as early as 1958, and negotiations with a large number of school districts continued through early 1959. By June, all necessary centers had been found and staffed, and this phase of the project was well in hand.

The academic year 1958–59 was a turbulent one for SMSG. The Group had come a long way from the resolution adopted by conferences of research mathematicians in Chicago and Cambridge. What the Yale writing session had proved to be possible had been rendered probable by the strenuous, year-long efforts of the headquarters staff. The time of the writing was at hand.

4 Second Writing Session

If one person can write a textbook and teacher's manual in four years, and another can write a textbook and teacher's manual in three years, and so on, how long will it take 101 people to write six textbooks and six teacher's manuals? This question, or one very much like it, confronted SMSG in June 1959. The answer had to be less than or equal to nine weeks (in mathematical parlance, this was an upper bound), because a large number of classrooms had to be supplied with the finished product very soon, and the printers had established firm deadlines to be met if their part of the job was to be accomplished on time. The figure of 101 writers was also somewhat high because not all the participants could be present all the time, many of them having other responsibilities for portions of the summer.

To complicate the problem further, the textbooks had to be good textbooks. They had to contain good mathematics, presented in a teachable manner, and made as interesting to the student as it was hoped it would be to the teachers. The books had to contain sets of exercises that would promote the students' facility in routine mathematical manipulations, while at the same time deepening their understanding of the concepts involved. Many of the exercises had to be of a "discovery" type that would extend the treatment in the text, and promote original thinking and creativity on the part of the student. The teacher's commentary that would accompany each text would have to contain, in addition to the solution of every exercise, as much background help and as many teaching suggestions as it was possible to provide, since there was to be much in the textbooks that would be as new to the teacher as to the student.

It has been said that the qualities of a worthy physician are three: the heart of a lion, the hand of a woman, and the eye of an eagle. From the foregoing list of demands to be made upon him, it seems apparent that the attributes of a qualified writer for SMSG would have to include not only the heart, the hand, and the eye but also the mathematical background of a Hilbert, the cunning of a Machiavelli, the speed of a hare, the teaching ability of a Socrates, the patience of a Job, and the stamina of a horse. As will be seen later, the addition of the hide of a rhinoceros to the list would not be inappropriate.

Since no one possessing all the desirable traits could be found, Professor Begle obtained the best first-approximations he could. These included the distinguished participants at Yale and an additional group of highly qualified mathematicians and high school teachers of no less imposing credentials than their earlier-starting colleagues. The writers were recruited all through the academic year. The mathematicians represented such diverse specializations as number theory, topology, applied mathematics, and modern algebra. The high school teachers and supervisors represented schools large and small, east, west, north, and south, rural and urban, public and private. Professional testing experts were obtained to help provide the best possible sets of exercises and sample testing items for the teacher's commentaries. Professional draftsmen were ready to provide graphs and charts, and eight mathematical typists, representing six states of the nation, were poised to go to work on first drafts.

The 7th and 8th grade subgroup, with membership expanded from eight to twenty-five, was to hold its writing session at the University of Michigan in Ann Arbor.[1] There were

1. See Appendix, List 17.

Second Writing Session

some housing difficulties to be settled because the University of Michigan had a rule forbidding children in the dormitories. This meant that individual housing had to be obtained for participants who wished to bring children. The single participants and those bringing only their spouses were quartered in the south and west quadrangles of the campus. In accord with SMSG's now standard policy, school and college teachers, except those living off campus, were quartered together. Working space was set up in Angell Hall, a block and a half from the living quarters.

On June 13-14, 1959, immediately prior to the first day of the writing session, the panel on 7th and 8th grades held a meeting at Dearborn, Michigan. The purpose of the meeting was to review the results of the year's experimental teaching, and to lay specific plans for the writing to be done during the summer. The members of the panel found that the comments of the teachers who had used the material were very favorable toward most of the units. More than 90 per cent of the reporting teachers recommended the inclusion of Units 1, 2, 3, 4, 5, 6, 10, 11, 12, and 13 (see page 24) in texts for 7th and 8th grades. In some few instances it was suggested that a unit be included in the 8th grade course only, or else as a supplement. Unit 8 was a case in point. There were too few reports on Units 4a, 9, and 14 upon which to base a conclusion. There were specific comments made about each unit. These concerned, among other things, time necessary to teach, level of difficulty, quality of writing, teachability, and whether supplementary material seemed appropriate. An interesting sidelight to these were several instances in which the same topic had been labeled "most teachable" by some and "most difficult" by others, "most interesting" by some and "least interesting" by others. There were reports from as many as 75 teachers on some units, and reports were still coming in.

On the basis of such information as was available from the tryouts, and the collective judgment of the panel, an outline was prepared for a course at the 7th grade level. Time did not

63

SMSG: The Making of a Curriculum

permit the detailed outlining of chapters or agreement on their order. In any event, the outline was only tentative, since the entire writing group would want to review the recommendation. Following some additional decisions regarding working procedures, time schedules, and format, the meeting of the panel adjourned, and the members moved over to Ann Arbor to join the ranks of the writers.

The first two days of the Ann Arbor writing session were given over to talks and group discussion. The addition of 17 new members to the 7th and 8th grade subgroup necessitated a review, for their benefit, of some of the problems worked out at Yale the preceding summer. The new members had earlier received copies of the units produced at Yale, so they were familiar with the general nature of the material. What they were not familiar with, and what the bland pages of finished text did not reflect, was the long sequence of drafts and discussions that went into the production of almost every unit. This knowledge, however, was not long withheld. After the writers had spent two days in examining the tentative outline set up by the panel, and started the work of revising the experimental units and compiling the 7th grade text, the dialogue resumed where it had left off at Yale. This time, however, more voices were involved, and some new units written during the academic year were more grist for the mill.

This subgroup had two tasks. The writers were to use the units written at Yale as a point of departure and prepare a complete sample textbook for grade 7. In addition, they were to produce additional units for testing that might, the following year, be incorporated into a text for grade 8. A commentary for teachers was to accompany each chapter in the text or each experimental unit. The operating procedures adopted for writing were substantially the same as those used at Yale. Writing teams composed of two or three persons, always including at least one college and one junior high school teacher or supervisor, undertook the first drafts. The writers had before them the comments of the teachers who had used the ma-

Second Writing Session

terial in the classroom during the experimental period. Indeed, many of the classroom teachers on the writing teams had taught both the Yale and Maryland materials.

The writing teams distributed duplicated copies of their work to all members of the 7th and 8th grade subgroup for written comment and criticism. Following tentative completion of a chapter, a hearing was held with the entire writing session in attendance for detailed critical discussion. The small writing team then convened to consider what to do about the various suggestions, and, using its own judgment, revised what it had written. So far, the modus operandi was the same as it had been at Yale. An additional safeguard was provided at this point, however, in an effort to achieve a completely smooth product. A coordinating committee was appointed and given the responsibility of preparing the manuscript for final production. This committee was invested with decisive authority on style, and it occupied a strong advisory position on content. When the writing team was satisfied with a chapter, and after the chapter had been through a subgroup hearing, it was sent to the coordinating committee. The writing team could; if it wished, join the coordinating committee as it read the material, standardized style and technique to blend with the rest of the book, and checked mathematical content to make sure that all necessary prerequisites would be met and duplications eliminated.

The writers were assigned desks in a large room, and the coordinating committee had desks in a smaller adjoining room. For the most part, the weather in Ann Arbor was quite warm in 1959, and some of the writers found it preferable to work in their own rooms or seek a vacant spot in the air-conditioned building adjoining Angell Hall. Writing is an individual act, and although teams of two were responsible for a finished unit or chapter, both members could not be writing on the same material at the same time. Each writer, therefore, had to seek the working conditions that were most conducive to production, and these conditions did not always prevail in the working area provided. The value of having teams of two or three working on a single unit lay in the speed with which first drafts could be produced. The college member of the team could check the mathematics in the material written by the classroom teacher or supervisor, while the latter could check the appropriateness of the material written by the college teacher for the students at the chosen grade level.

Writing textual material of the kind produced by SMSG requires a talent not possessed by everyone. The fact that a person is a gifted research mathematician, a gifted classroom teacher, or an efficient supervisor in no way guarantees that he or she can construct a paragraph of good textual material. Similarly, the fact that a person can sit down with a pencil and paper and pour forth literate prose in no way guarantees that the prose has any worthwhile content or that it will be of interest or value to an audience. It happened, therefore, that some members of the writing team did little or none of the actual writing but served in capacities no less vital to the completion of the project as critics, advisors, or exercise writers.

To ensure that the teacher's commentaries were ready when the texts were ready, each writing team had to present both text and the accompanying teacher's commentary to the coordinating committee at the same time. Since the first third of the book had to be in the hands of the printer in typed form ready for photographing before the close of the writing session, the coordinating committee established a firm and very early deadline for their reception of the first third of the material from the writers. As the pressure for completed manuscript rose, the full group meetings held to review the efforts of the writing teams were reduced to meetings of those members of the group who felt they had something important to contribute. This reduction proved so efficient that at the end of the session, the group recommended that, in any future activities of a similar kind, all group reviews be limited to volunteers only.

When the Ann Arbor writing session closed on August 7,

Second Writing Session

1959, the participants had managed to meet every deadline. They had produced Volume I of *Junior High School Mathematics,* a text proposed for students at the 7th grade level. They had also completed a series of sample units which the subgroup considered suitable for inclusion in an 8th grade text and which were to be bound together in a single volume, Volume II of *Junior High School Mathematics.* These volumes would be tested both individually and sequentially during the 1959–60 academic year, and the sample 8th grade text would be written the following summer.

Volumes I and II were accompanied by teacher's commentaries. Both volumes emphasized the structure of arithmetic, the real number system as a progressing development, and metric and nonmetric relations in geometry. These ideas were constantly associated with their applications. Included, also, were some units on measurement, statistics, numeration, and probability, together with many sections of applications and motivational material. The 7th and 8th grade subgroup had looked upon the 7th and 8th grades as a place for exploration and transition, a bridging of the gap between grades 6 and 9. They agreed, therefore, that the mathematics offered at this level should be more than a hone upon which to sharpen elementary school skills, and more than a place to begin high school mathematics early. They felt that grade 7 should begin where grade 6 leaves off, and that its content should carefully lay the groundwork for both the algebra and geometry that follow in the high school.

In addition, they hoped to present to the students who would not be enrolling in the academic sequence some basic skills that would be sufficiently general and flexible to cope with many of the mathematical situations in which they might one day find themselves. They hoped to interest all students, of all degrees of mathematical aptitude, in the further study of the subject. The problem of evaluating the achievement of these goals was a difficult matter and one whose solution might ultimately depend upon the work of many years. How-

SMSG: The Making of a Curriculum

ever, the experimental centers were waiting, the texts and manuals were ready, and the coming academic year would produce at least some indication of how well they had succeeded.

The 1959 writing session for the 9th through 12th grades began one week after that of the 7th and 8th grades. It was held on the campus of the University of Colorado, in Boulder. There was a total of 76 participants in this session, as compared to the 37 who worked on the same levels at Yale.[2] The facilities available were ideal. Not only were most of the participants (and the families of those who wished to bring them) housed in one dormitory, but the third floor of the same building was given over to working space for the project. Thus, one building, Hallett Hall, served as home and office for each participant. The only traveling necessary for the writers was the trek of a few hundred feet to Libby Hall for meals. It would be difficult to imagine a situation more suitable for the sort of close cooperation necessary in such a project. To minimize the possible distraction of some of the participants by the children of others, all families with smaller children were lodged on the lower floor of the building. There were two ping-pong tables located there, as well as a large open room in which children could play.

It had been suggested at some of the planning sessions for the summer of 1959 that, since the experience at Yale had shown that many participants would be prone to work every night and every weekend if nothing was done to discourage it, Professor Begle made sure that no meals were served in the dining room on either Saturday or Sunday. This would force participants to leave the campus at least briefly. Better than this, however, was Professor Begle's foresight in obtaining the services of Robert Ellingwood, of the Applied Mathematics Department of the University of Colorado, who combined all that was best of mathematician, administrator, and mountaineer. Mr. Ellingwood acted as SMSG's liaison with the uni-

2. See Appendix, List 17.

Second Writing Session

versity in matters of housing, equipment, and supplies. In addition, as recreation director for the session, he planned hiking and camping expeditions to nearby spots in the Rockies. Beginning with a short two- or three-hour picnic trip the first Sunday after the opening of the session, he planned progressively more demanding jaunts, culminating with a two-day expedition to the top of Long's Peak. A surprisingly large number of the participants in the session took advantage of the opportunities offered by these trips to leave the cares and problems of the written word behind.

The writing session at Boulder began on Monday morning, June 22. After a brief general meeting, each grade-level subgroup immediately convened. With the addition of so many new members, each of the subgroups was faced with the problem of re-establishing within itself a common viewpoint (or a reasonable approximation of such) with which to begin work. This meant, in many cases, another trip across the same philosophical and pedagogical landscape traversed so patiently the year before at Yale. In most such trips, the destination reached was much the same as the one reached before, and, in general, the discussions were briefer. The fact that one-third of a completed manuscript was due in the hands of the typists on July 15 was ever before the participants.

Each of the grade-level subgroups adopted its own working procedures. The 9th grade writers opened the session with a group meeting to consider the Yale outline and the two or three chapters that had been written during the academic year. It developed that though the group still viewed the Yale outline as satisfactory, there were some modifications of points of view that rendered the interim work unusable. Consequently the entire 9th grade textbook had to be rewritten. The general session of the subgroup was not extensive, and work on the actual writing began very quickly. The first drafts of the various chapters were written by teams of from two to five or six people, including, as always, both college and high school teachers. As in the 7th and 8th grade subgroups, early drafts were duplicated and distributed to a whole subgroup, and sometimes meetings of the subgroups were called to review and criticize the material written by the small writing teams. More often, each member of the subgroup was encouraged to write directly on a copy of the material such criticism or comment as seemed indicated, and then return the copy to the writing team for its consideration. In some cases, a person with a different view of a topic would rewrite a whole section. In addition to these formal critical procedures, there was always much informal discussion. As was the case within previous subgroups, not all of the team members wrote. Some of them devoted their time to exercises, some to proofreading, and some to careful criticism of what was written. One person did all the final writing.[3] This sometimes meant just the editorial work of polishing, but frequently it meant a considerable amount of rewriting. A high order of ingenuity was required of the final writer in order to resolve the often conflicting viewpoints of two or more people on the same topic.

Unlike the 7th and 8th grade subgroup, the 9th grade writers did not attempt to produce textual material and teacher's commentary at the same time. The teacher's commentary for the 9th grade was written by a large number of people, sometimes by the same team that wrote the corresponding textual material, but frequently by others. There was not time to have the commentary reproduced and circulated for comment, but at least two high school teachers or supervisors and two college people reviewed each section of it. No single person, however, wrote the final draft on this.

When the 10th grade subgroup convened on the first day, they found themselves in a very advantageous position. Professor Moise had completed, during the spring semester of 1959, a first draft of the proposed textbook. As soon as it was written, a copy of each chapter had been mailed to each member of the subgroup, so that they were kept continuously informed as to the status of their project. In addition, members

3. Vincent Haag, of Franklin and Marshall College.

Second Writing Session

of this subgroup held a meeting in New York on May 9, at which they discussed the work that had been done and laid specific plans for the work of the coming summer. Therefore, when the writing session began, the group as a whole had much to discuss, and went to work on Professor Moise's first draft, chapter by chapter. Controversial subject matter and methods of approach in each chapter were pinpointed, and these matters were settled by the entire group. Editorial comments on sentence structure, syntax, and the like, were postponed until later. Following a discussion of each chapter, the revision of that chapter was begun. Five working teams were designated: for text, teacher's commentary, exercises, editing, and problems of organization and coordinating (one person).

While each chapter of the text was being revised, the teacher's commentary material paralleling this chapter was begun, and exercise sets were devised for each section in the chapter. As soon as a second draft of a chapter was completed it was duplicated and circulated to each member of the subgroup for written comments and criticism. To ensure that the rigid deadlines for finished material were met, any criticism or comments on a given section had to be returned to the writing team within 48 hours. A similar time limitation was placed on criticism of exercise and teacher's commentary copy.

When the second draft had been revised in the light of the written comments received, the final copy of text, exercise sets, and teacher's commentary was sent to the editorial team to be made ready for final typing. The coordinating "team" (perhaps production manager would be a more appropriate term) was responsible for seeing that all drafts of all material reached the proper hands, and that work progressed smoothly. Chapter after chapter passed through this procedure until, by the end of the session, both textbook and teacher's commentary were in final form and dispatched to the printer.

The 11th grade subgroup, suffering as it did from an embarrassment of riches in the form of content, fell on its work with urgency and vigor. This subgroup had devised a scheme whereby it hoped to avoid the necessity of lengthy group meetings. Rather than organizing on an overall basis of writers, editors, critics, and exercise constructors, its membership split into sections. Each section, called a "chapter team," was composed of college and high school teachers. Each chapter team had a chairman who was responsible for the production of his team. Writers were designated for each team, and one or two persons were asked to consult with the writer while the writing was going on. First drafts were circulated only within the team concerned. Because there were only 18 members of the subgroup, and 16 chapters, each member of the subgroup had to serve on a number of teams. Coordination between teams was achieved by the appointment of section chairmen. For example, the first four chapters were under the jurisdiction of one such chairman, the next three under another, and so on. Each participant had a primary responsibility on certain chapter teams, either as writer or exercise writer and solver, as well as a secondary responsibility on others, either as critic or exercise writer and solver.

After material was written it sometimes became necessary to have meetings of chapter teams, but when these were held, the participants who were not members of this particular team could continue with their work. Such meetings almost inevitably resulted in a revision of the original material. When a team had what it considered a suitable chapter, the material was labeled a semifinal draft and turned over to the chairman of the team, who in turn passed it on to the appropriate section chairman. It was the responsibility of the section chairman to review the draft to make sure it merged both in content and prose with the other chapters in his section. Having satisfied himself on this score, he then submitted the draft to a panel of readers who had been asked to judge the teachability of the chapters. Following this, a final check was made by a mathematician to ascertain that no mathematical errors had escaped detection.

When all these reviews had been made, the draft was re-

Second Writing Session

turned to the chapter team for revision. The final draft was then sent from chapter chairman to section chairman to subgroup chairman, who referred it to an editorial panel for final review. This review was concerned with form and style rather than content. The draft was then returned to the subgroup chairman for approval and finally sent to the typists. The teacher's commentary for each chapter was prepared by the chapter team and was usually written by the individual who had served as principal writer for the chapter. This material was reviewed in the same manner as the textbook copy, although it did not prove possible to spend quite as much time on it.

Though the system used by the 11th grade group appears complex, it should be remembered that this group had a particularly heavy job with respect to topics, and, by keeping a close and continuous check on the flow of material, the members found that the plan worked well and enabled them to meet the deadlines set for them.

The 12th grade group found itself in relatively good shape. Interim work had produced revisions of two of the chapters written at Yale and some new first draft material on some of the remaining chapters. In addition, an alternative outline had been developed for their volume, *An Introduction to Modern Algebra,* which approached the topic from a different point of view.

The initial meeting of the entire subgroup was, therefore, brief and was largely concerned with designating work for each participant. Some decisions had to be made, however, about the approach to be used in one or two topics and about the emphasis to be placed on the topic of sets. These matters did not prove troublesome, and the one major decision facing the group was on content of the second semester course. Two outlines now existed for a course in modern algebra. After some careful consideration, the decision was made to discard both outlines and write a book on matrix algebra. This decision sprang, in part, from the fact that the subject of matrix

73

algebra maintained contact with the concrete and practical problem of solving systems of linear equations. But, more than this, the algebra of matrices led more naturally and easily into the topics of groups, rings, and fields (the backbone of modern algebra) than did the courses previously outlined.

Once this decision was made, the subgroup was divided into two sections, a large section to work on the first semester course on elementary functions, and a smaller group to work on the matrix algebra. One person was to serve as production manager for both groups. Since the 12th grade group had been enlarged only from 8 members to 13, and since two of the five new additions were not really new (they had worked on other grade levels the previous summer), the work to be done was already very familiar to most of the group, and they could take up where they had left off at Yale.

The writing was done by teams of two or three college and high school people working together. Successive drafts of material were circulated to all members of the subgroup for criticism, and then revised by the original writing team. When a final draft was generally acceptable, it was sent to an editorial panel for standardization of style and format, and then to the typists for final typing. Exercises and material were, for the most part, written by the writing team that wrote the text, as was the material for the teacher's commentary. There were some exceptions to this, particularly with respect to compiling solutions to the exercises for the teacher's commentary, but, where possible, the same writers wrote the material for both student and teacher. The number of subgroup meetings was held to a minimum, perhaps two or three during the entire session, and these were convened only if a matter of great importance was involved. For example, one such meeting dealt with the best approach to teaching the trigonometric functions.

The writers of the matrix algebra formed almost a distinct subgroup of their own, since they were writing a distinct book. The work was directed by Edwin F. Beckenbach, of the Uni-

Second Writing Session

versity of California, Los Angeles, and the RAND Corporation. Though, on occasion, there was much cross-fertilization among the writers of the two volumes, it was generally true that each of the teams solved its own problems, and felt a primary responsibility for just one project. The size of the matrix algebra writing team was such that work on the teacher's commentary for this course had to be continued through the early fall, although both books, *Elementary Functions* and *Introduction to Matrix Algebra,* were ready for use in the experimental centers in September, as was the teacher's commentary for the first book.

In addition to the work of the subgroups, a team of experts on testing was engaged in the construction of sample items for tests to be included in the teacher's commentary. They were working with all grade levels, and, consequently, might be considered ex officio members of all subgroups.

To appreciate fully what was accomplished at Ann Arbor and Boulder in the summer of 1959, it is necessary to know something more than the manner in which the subgroups organized themselves or the physical conditions under which they worked. Although the writing procedures varied from subgroup to subgroup, the role of the individual participant was much the same at all grade levels. It should be kept in mind that each subgroup had to write a complete textbook and teacher's commentary in two months. This is a project that, under normal circumstances, with two or three collaborators, is usually distributed over a period of two or three years, with work proceeding only when convenient to the writers. Though the total man hours devoted to writing the SMSG textbooks would probably be as high or higher than the total needed to write a commercial text, the hours were compressed into a two-month period. The writers for SMSG, therefore, had to be skilled enough to be able to produce first-rate material in a steady and continuous stream.

A glance at the list of participants is sufficient to show that such was indeed the case. Many of them were writers of recog-

SMSG: The Making of a Curriculum

nized stature and long experience in the production of mathematical textbooks. Almost all of them had contributed articles to professional journals. There was certainly no lack of experience in the personnel. On the other hand, few of them had ever been called upon to write under circumstances even remotely similar to those facing them that summer.

Writing textbooks, as anyone who has done it will attest, is a difficult and demanding task. Though some persons can produce material faster than others, it is never done without considerable effort and expenditure of energy. One writer may sit and stare at an empty page for several hours and then, in a burst of effort over a very short period of time, produce as much material as another who has written steadily at a constant rate for the entire period. One writer may produce a first draft that is virtually flawless, whereas another may produce a hodge-podge of disorganized ideas expressed in fractured syntax, which he can then rewrite into a second draft of acceptable caliber. Indeed, the second writer might produce two drafts in the time it takes the first to produce one. The point to be made here is that the writers differed among themselves in working habits as much as the subgroups did in organization. It was the job of the subgroup chairman to determine the optimum use of the wide variety of talents and types he had within his subgroup, subject, of course, to the desires of the participant. Almost universally, the participants readily agreed to assume such work as would best serve the interests of the group, and they left this decision to their chairman.

Those selected to write first drafts had to be prepared for criticism of their efforts of an almost unprecedented intensity. It is not too much to assert that the critical reading of SMSG material prior to its publication exceeded that devoted to any similar textbooks ever produced, with respect to both quantity and quality. It was significant that the material was carefully read by qualified people who were on the scene. Every point in question could be examined by many experts, and, when necessary, full-scale subgroup meetings could be con-

Second Writing Session

vened to devote further attention to the matter. This is a kind of critical examination that is just not feasible under any but the circumstances that existed at SMSG writing sessions. The criticism of a writer's first draft was usually devastating, and it took persons of great character and dedicated purpose to accept it cheerfully and carry on with the preparation of a second draft. In many cases, a writer had to be prepared to see his work completely rewritten by another person, who, in turn, might have his effort rewritten by a third. One writer, upon seeing some material he had originally written come across his desk in fourth draft form, remarked that all he could find remaining from his treatment were the punctuation marks!

This continuous writing and rewriting, discussion and criticism, suggesting and commenting was the very essence of SMSG production. No one, regardless of his race, creed, or academic rank, produced material that was immune from the searching, critical eyes of his colleagues, and yet the deep consciousness of purpose that permeated the writing sessions mitigated against irresponsible or personal criticism. Occasionally, in the published reviews of commercial textbooks (or perhaps more frequently in the unpublished reviews) a reviewer indulges in the demolition of a writer's efforts solely to display his personal bias or to exploit the space given to him for review by extolling the merits of his own, sometimes curious, point of view. Though such reviews are frequently interesting to read, all too often they are neither accurate nor instructive and, at best, serve only to amuse momentarily. There was little room for this sort of display in SMSG criticism. If the reader could not see a specific way to improve the treatment or was not prepared to attempt his own version, there was nothing to be gained by indulging his personal sense of whimsy, and, even had any readers been so inclined, there was nobody present who would have been amused by it.

There was more than enough constructive advice to go around. Writers would frequently be faced with suggestions

SMSG: The Making of a Curriculum

from two different sources based on diametrically opposed points of view. It was not unusual in such cases for the writer to bring the two critics together and ask them to reconcile their differences and then report on such agreement as was reached so that the next draft could be completed. Sometimes criticism would come from a college teacher who felt that a treatment did not go deeply enough into a topic, while at the same time a high school teacher would reject the whole topic as unteachable. It was this constant meticulous examination of every paragraph that ultimately led to the finished text, and, though no member of SMSG felt inclined or obligated to agree with every treatment of every topic at every grade level, he could still assert that the books as a whole presented a vivid picture of what he considered good mathematics, suitable for a curriculum for college-capable high school students. This, after all, was the purpose of the project.

Overall supervision of the work of the writing sessions was in the hands of Professor Begle. Headquarters operations for SMSG were temporarily moved to Boulder so that he could remain with the session. He met frequently with the grade level chairmen to check on progress and to help overcome any difficulties arising in the course of the writing. His duties as director, however, included considerations other than the writing of the texts, for he had also to take care of many problems in connection with the printing of the texts, experimental centers, the monograph project, and so on.

When the Ann Arbor writing session closed, John Wagner immediately flew to Boulder to assist Professor Begle in the problems associated with the printing and testing of the finished textbooks. At this time there remained two weeks of the Boulder session, and Professor Begle could devote more time to expediting the writing, since the pressure of time was becoming increasingly critical. The first third of each course, together with teacher's commentary, had been finished and sent off on August 1 on schedule, but the material for the last two-

Second Writing Session

thirds of each course had to be ready for typing when the session closed on August 21.

The eight typists secured by SMSG for the summer proved to be too few to cope with the enormous amount of material. Not only were there four or five drafts of each chapter of each textbook to be typed on reproducing masters, but the final copy, typed on a special paper for photography, had to be letter perfect. More typists were secured, and the wives of some of the participants were pressed into service on a part-time basis. One person was charged with the responsibility of supervising all the work of the typists at Boulder, as well as the reproduction of written material and the distribution of all supplies to the writers.[4] All manuscripts passed through his hands and were allotted to typists on the basis of a priority system, designed to keep the most important materials flowing freely and to ensure that each typist received the type of material she was best qualified to handle. Runners were available to distribute each draft to those concerned with it, and this distribution was governed by master distribution lists maintained in the clerical staff office.

Before leaving the discussion of the Boulder writing session, something more should be said about the way of life in a writing session. As at Yale, the sharing of living facilities and the presence of the families of the participants did much to bolster the feeling of mutual purpose that each participant had. The recreation program promoted by Mr. Ellingwood also made a significant contribution to this feeling. On the lighter side, ping-pong and badminton served as means of working off the tension of the day's work. The favorite Japanese game of Go attracted the attention of some of the writers, and the Go boards inscribed with their starkly plain coordinate systems were much in evidence. While the writing session was in progress, Burton W. Jones, Chairman of the Department of Pure Mathematics at the University of Colorado, was conducting a research seminar for number theorists, and the seminar partici-

---

4. John W. Stevens, of New Haven, Connecticut.

SMSG: The Making of a Curriculum

pants were housed in the dormitory nearest Hallett Hall. There was much intermingling of the people working with SMSG and the seminar participants, and evening conversations might switch abruptly from problems in the theory of numbers to problems in the teaching of plane geometry.

The atmosphere, then, in which the first sample textbooks for SMSG were written, was one of high purpose and dedication and steeped in a spirit of enjoyment of the subject. The work was demanding but welcome, and was never far from the minds of all concerned. Even the children were drawn upon for help, and sometimes one or two of the younger set were plucked from the badminton court and requested to read some material whose clarity or teachability was questionable. If subsequent questioning revealed that the concept had not been mastered, that section was returned to the writer to be rewritten in clearer form. Furthermore, the children were sometimes asked to check writing style. Was it interesting? Did it make them want to know more about the subject? Would they enjoy studying from a textbook written in this manner?

The question of style was a troublesome one and, except for those groups using a single writer on final draft, caused the members of early editorial committees considerable difficulty. There are several schools of thought on how to write textbook prose, and almost all of them had representation in SMSG. A writer might find, on the same bit of material, directions from one critic, "Suggest you alter this chatty tone," while from another, "This seems to have been written by a machine." As time went by, the writers came to a kind of instinctive understanding with regard to style that persisted in later drafts.

At the close of the writing session at Boulder, SMSG possessed a complete set of textbooks covering all grade levels from 7 through 12. These books would exhibit to the educational world an example of a mathematics curriculum for college-capable students that SMSG thought suitable for today's needs. There was no thought then, or ever, in the minds

Second Writing Session

of anyone associated with this effort, that this was the only or best curriculum. It was simply a concrete example of course material they deemed appropriate to the times. Though they had no doubt that the mathematics in the textbooks was good mathematics, there remained the question of whether it could be taught. The high school teachers had, in each team, done their very best to ensure that it could. But whereas the mathematicians could reduce the sort of problems they dealt with to objective, logical arguments, the teachers could only operate within the area of their combined experience with high school students, and, as always in matters of this kind, there was a margin for error. It remained for the experimental centers to determine how close they had come to the truth.

5 Tryout and Revision of Sample Textbooks

There is an old saw to the effect that the proof of the pudding is in the eating. When autumn came in 1959, SMSG was in possession of a very large pudding indeed—the completed manuscripts of six textbooks and a number of individual units. It remained to see the reaction of 26,000 students in 49 centers.

Two-thirds of each text and each teacher's manual were yet to come, however, and, because of the pressure on typists for preliminary drafts of material, there had been no time for typing this material at Boulder. Therefore, when the Boulder writing session ended and SMSG returned its headquarters to Yale University, the final untyped drafts were shipped back to Yale. As soon as the staff reopened regular headquarters in New Haven, it was necessary to hire eight more typists to type copy for photographing. At the same time, other typists in St. Paul, Minnesota, Emporia, Kansas, and Los Angeles, California, were set to work on some of the material. It was not until February 1960 that the last of the copy was sent to the printer.

Four printers were used for the first third of the material, one located in the West, one in the East, and two in the Midwest, to facilitate printing and distribution.

Some of the sample textbooks were printed in three volumes and some in two, and the respective volumes were timed to arrive at the centers so that the teaching of the courses could

Sample Books

proceed in a smooth and uninterrupted manner. Except for a few isolated instances of delay in the distribution of the books, the system worked extremely well, and was the only one possible if the tests were to be conducted during the school semester following the writing.

The best evidence of what was being tested is, as the lawyers put it, *res ipsa,* the thing itself. An inspection of the contents of the books is the best means of determining just what it was the writers were trying to do; however, a brief preliminary discussion of each might prove helpful. It will be recalled that the controversy over the traditional 7th and 8th grade curricular offerings centered about the amount of review and rote drill involved, the picture of the nature of mathematics that was being presented, and the types of applications of mathematics being used. The 7th grade text produced at Ann Arbor differed dramatically from the usual offerings at this level. It began with an exploration into the concerns of mathematics, and observed therein that computation, as such, was only one of many facets of the subject, and that the principal ingredient of mathematics was reasoning, both inductive (from the specific to the general) and deductive (from the general to the specific). The text quickly moved into specific subject matter starting with numeration (the representation of numbers by symbols). Various numeration systems were used to illustrate basic properties, and a historical presentation showed the development of our present system of numeration.

There followed a development of the basic structural components of the whole numbers, some informal geometry, and a thorough and meaningful treatment of rational numbers and the fractions that name them. The emphasis throughout the text was on mathematics rather than applications, although applications appeared here and there in the exercises, and quite heavily in the unit on percentage. Percentage was approached by means of proportion, and the common practice of separating the topic into special cases was completely avoided. The book was written in a lively and discursive way

SMSG: The Making of a Curriculum

and showed the results of a great deal of thought on the part of the writers with respect to motivation.

The 8th grade volume was not really considered a textbook but rather a series of experimental units, although it was bound as a single volume. Among the topics covered were coordinate systems, linear equations, scientific notation, metric geometry, real numbers, and areas and volumes of plane figures and solids. There were also units dealing with measurement and statistics. As a result of the year's experimenting, a sequential text would be written for the 8th grade at the next writing session.

The SMSG 9th grade algebra differed from the traditional algebra textbook in many ways, although content was not one of them. The topics discussed were essentially conventional. The approach was very different, and placed emphasis on a clear-cut and mathematically sound picture of the structure of algebra. There were 14 chapters in the finished textbook, and they covered algebra through quadratic equations. The expository material was characterized by a sense of sharing, by the writer and the reader, of the discovery of the properties of a number system. It was written in a warm and friendly tone that leaned heavily on a kind of Socratic questioning and led, insofar as possible, to the discovery of basic properties by the student. Later in the book, when sufficient groundwork had been laid, the student was introduced to deductive proofs, and these were then used to place the facts discovered by intuition or observation on a sound logical footing. Set concepts and set notation were used wherever they would lend clarity or precision to a topic, and served as a means of relating numbers and geometric points. The book exhibited a striking departure in spirit from traditional algebra books.

The 10th grade geometry book adhered closely to the outline described earlier in Chapter 2. It was marked by accurate language, precisely worded postulates, definitions, and theorems, a fusing of plane and solid geometry, and a combination of formal and intuitive reasoning calculated to display to the

Sample Books

student the appealing nature of mathematics. It contained 16 chapters and eight appendices, the appendices consisting of optional material. The teacher's commentary accompanying the textbook contained, in addition to a running commentary on the text, six units entitled "Talks to Teachers," which were unique in SMSG writings at the time. These talks dealt with concepts that cut across two or more topics in the course, and were written for the purpose of supplying the teacher with mathematical depth and background in difficult areas. They were to prove very popular and were incorporated into certain later teacher's commentaries in other courses.

The 11th grade textbook, entitled *Intermediate Mathematics*, was the longest textbook produced by SMSG during the writing session. It consisted of 15 chapters in 799 pages, and covered much trigonometry as well as algebra. It began with a very complete yet concise redevelopment of the system of real numbers studied in beginning algebra. From here, the analytic geometry of the plane was introduced and the function concept was developed and explored in some detail. Among the topics dealt with at this grade level were such things as simultaneous systems, sequences, logarithmic, exponential, and trigonometric functions, and mathematical induction. The trigonometric functions were introduced from the standpoint of angle measure, as opposed to the 12th grade development in terms of arc length. The book contained very solid mathematics, and was the SMSG text around which the greatest number of questions of scope and difficulty hovered. The reports of its acceptance in the classroom were eagerly awaited.

The 12th grade subgroup produced two textbooks. The first-semester text, *Elementary Functions,* contained five chapters and seven short appendices. The content is suggested by the title. The book began with a chapter that carefully developed the function concept from the standpoint of sets. The chapter was included largely because it was felt that students using this text at the experimental centers would be doing so

SMSG: The Making of a Curriculum

without the benefit of previous experience with sets or set concepts. There followed a treatment of polynominal functions, exponential functions, logarithmic functions, and circular functions, the latter from the standpoint of arc length instead of angles as in 11th grade texts. As was the case with all other SMSG sample textbooks, the emphasis was on clear, concise language and on the structural properties of the subject matter. The second-semester textbook, *Introduction to Matrix Algebra,* contained five chapters, together with a section of what were termed "Research Exercises," a number of interesting and difficult extensions of the ideas developed in the book. These exercises were designed to challenge the very best students, and were not to be considered a part of the regular course. The book was also written in a lively, readable style, and marked the first known attempt to treat the subject of matrices in any detail at the high school level.

These, then, were the sample textbooks whose teachability was to be tested in the experimental centers. These were the media through which SMSG hoped eventually to exert an influence on the school mathematics curriculum. Individually and in the total, they exhibited a program markedly different from the traditional one. More than this, the books themselves had features unusual in comparable books. For one thing, the presentation made no use of color, illustration, or any of the production features widely prevalent at the time. This is understandable, of course, since the printing costs had to be kept minimal, and there was no thought of having the books competitive with those produced commercially. But the fact remains that the pages of the books were stark, typewritten sheets, and any appeal they would have for students and teachers would have to be by merit of their contents.

For another thing, they contained an unusual amount of expository writing compared with traditional textbooks. SMSG texts contained about six or seven times the usual explanatory material and made unprecedented demands on reading ability. Most commercial texts of the time had the briefest possible

Sample Books

written explanations, preferring to teach largely by means of solved sample problems (the emphasis on manipulations, as mentioned by critics). The SMSG participants did not share the philosophy behind such texts, and one of their tenets was that every student should be given an opportunity to learn to read mathematical literature, an experience different from reading prose of a nontechnical nature. Accordingly they provided the opportunity in every book they produced.

Still a third difference exhibited by SMSG texts lay in their size. They were printed on pages the same size as common typewriter paper. This, again, was a result of the need for speedy printing and economy. (Later the books were reduced to a more conventional size.) The books that were used in the experimental period were often alleged to contribute as much to the physical development of the student as to his mental development, simply because they had to be carried from place to place.

These were all matters that, presumably, might tend to militate against the success of the books in the classroom, and are therefore worth mentioning. It should be kept in mind that it was content that was being tested. If the content won acceptance, then it was almost certain that improved physical packages would follow.

The experimental centers of 1959–60 operated in much the same fashion as those used for the 7th and 8th grades throughout the academic year 1958–59.[1] One variation of the center concept was instituted under the title of "point." A point differed from a center in that no financial support was provided by SMSG other than the furnishing of experimental textbooks. If a community wished to use SMSG textbooks at one or another grade, and if they would agree to have the teachers return questionnaires to SMSG headquarters at the end of each chapter, then SMSG would consider their inclusion in the tryout program as a point. No locality, however,

1. See Appendix, List 18.

87

could be designated as a point if it did not agree to hire, with its own funds, a consulting mathematician for the teachers involved. The only exceptions were those cases where an SMSG writer was responsible for the point. The point concept was an outgrowth of the desire on the part of some of the SMSG writers to use SMSG materials in their own schools. Since the centers had been established prior to the Boulder writing session, no subsequent provision could be made for centers, but Professor Begle arranged for the establishment of points in response to the writers' requests. SMSG was supplying textbooks for about 40 centers during the 1959–60 academic year.

The insistence on the part of SMSG that all teachers trying the sample textbooks be supplied with consulting help by a mathematician is not strange. The books contained much that would be new to almost all high school teachers. If the content of the books was to have an honest trial, it was deemed essential that the teaching be done at least as well as in traditional classes. The best way to approximate this level of competence seemed to be to choose good teachers who wanted to teach the SMSG material, and then to provide them with all the help possible. A sure way to negate the hopes and efforts of all those who had labored to produce the sample books would be to have the material taught in a halfhearted or incompetent manner, and consequently have the books branded in high school circles as unteachable. Therefore, extreme care had to be taken that the trials be conducted in as fair a manner as possible. To say that the tryouts were "loaded" by choosing good teachers and then giving them every help is to have missed the point. All that was wanted was equality with traditional teaching of traditional materials as near as it could be obtained.

In this light, SMSG kept a very tight rein on the whole tryout program. Not only were the classroom teachers in the centers and points given assistance, but the experimental textbooks were not for sale in classroom quantities. After all the

Sample Books

testing classrooms were supplied with the necessary materials, the textbooks were made available to the public in limited quantities, but this was not until well on into the spring of 1960.

The orientation conference held in Washington, D.C., in 1958, for the teachers in the 7th and 8th grade centers had proved so valuable that another was held in Chicago on September 19, 1959. More than 98 per cent of all teachers and consultants in the experimental centers (not points, however) were present to participate.[2] Each of the subgroups had two or more representatives present, and, as before, the teachers who would be using the new textbooks were afforded the opportunity of discussing the content with the authors. It was made very clear to the teachers, as it had been the previous year, that SMSG was a team effort and that without the help and advice of the classroom teachers the whole effort would be of dubious value.

Most of the administrative detail associated with the operation of the experimental testing was the responsibility of Mr. Wagner. Also, following the writing session at Boulder, Robert Davis, of Syracuse University, was added to the staff on a two-thirds time basis to help with headquarters work. The activities of SMSG were expanding, and, in addition to the massive task of trying out the sample textbook, Professor Begle had to concern himself with new projects.

It will be recalled that, early in 1959, the appointment of a panel on elementary school mathematics had been recommended by the Advisory Committee, but work in this area had been postponed until after the summer writing session. Professor Begle appointed such a panel in November,[3] and the first meeting of this group was held in Chicago on January 30, 1960. The Advisory Committee had suggested that SMSG undertake a critical study of the elementary school mathematics curriculum from the point of view of (1) increased

2. See Appendix, List 19.
3. See Appendix, List 20.

emphasis on concepts and mathematical principles, (2) the grade placement of topics in arithmetic, (3) the introduction of new topics, and (4) supplementary topics for the better students. Funds had been budgeted for the inclusion of elementary school mathematics work in the third writing session of SMSG to be held in the summer of 1960. At the panel meeting it was decided to hold a planning session later in the winter to outline what was to be done. It was decided that grades 4 through 6 were the appropriate grades for consideration, and Professor Begle was asked to begin making arrangements for tryout centers in the fall.

The planning session was held in Chicago during the week March 5–12, 1960, and was attended by eleven persons who would be involved in the summer's writing.[4] These included all but two of the panel. The session produced rather detailed outlines for a number of units that the group thought appropriate for grade levels 4 through 6. Those outlines were to be expanded into teaching units in the coming writing session.

Another new panel of SMSG, that on non-college-bound students, held its first meeting at Boulder, Colorado, during the writing session there.[5] For a working classification, non-college-bound students were defined as those in the 25–75 per cent ability range, since it was felt that those students below the 25 per cent mark presented special problems. SMSG had chosen to confine its first efforts in curriculum reform to the college-capable student, for the reasons mentioned earlier. The curriculum content for students in the college-capable category was not difficult to define, but the problem relative to the non-college-bound students was more involved. Traditional practices in this area varied widely, and included everything from remedial drill in arithmetic processes to quite technical applications of mathematics to industrial shop work. Some books in use in this category were concerned with consumer applications, some with business applications, and some

4. See Appendix, List 21.
5. See Appendix, List 22.

Sample Books

with a wide variety of applications from home, field, and factory. Many of the books at the senior high school level contained mathematics that did not differ materially from that in textbooks at the junior high school level, and, as has been noted, this did not differ much from elementary school mathematics. In short, a good number of them were concerned with quite elementary arithmetic processes applied in a variety of relatively trivial ways.

In line with general SMSG policy, the panel agreed that it was not their function to determine a definitive course for such students, but rather to produce a sample of one or more types of courses that they considered suitable. They were concerned with two levels, the senior high school and junior high school. They were aware that SMSG had already produced materials at both levels for the college-capable student, materials rich in the powerful and pervasive fundamental concepts of mathematics. These basic ideas were deemed to be so important, from both a cultural and a utilitarian point of view, that the panel felt them appropriate to the needs of all students, and not merely those bound for college. There was a very real question, however, as to whether these concepts could be taught to students in the 25–75 per cent ability range. The members of the panel decided that if even a small amount of evidence could be obtained indicating that these concepts were accessible to this population, a large-scale effort to test the same hypothesis on a nationwide basis was justifiable.

Four of the members of the panel agreed to sponsor pilot classes in their communities in which the 7th and 8th grade materials would be tried out with students at a number of different grade levels and with a variety of backgrounds. Should the results of this small test show signs of success, the panel recommended that writing teams be put to work at the next summer's writing session at both the senior and junior high school levels to rewrite the existing 7th and 9th grade SMSG textbooks. The rewriting would try to present the subject at a slower rate and provide an increased number of care-

SMSG: The Making of a Curriculum

fully designed exercises. The rewritten textbooks could then be used on a wide scale to see whether the 25 to 75 per cent ability group could indeed learn valuable and significant mathematics.

The work of the panel on teacher training continued through the year. Vincent H. Haag, of Franklin and Marshall College, had agreed to write a volume for the series dealing with the algebra basic to the 9th grade course, and he was able to devote half his time during the spring semester of 1960 to this task. Under the direction of this panel, arrangements were made to have some Russian material translated for possible use by teachers in this country. A study guide in calculus was also planned.

The panel on 7th and 8th grades and the panel on sample textbooks studied the data flowing in from the experimental centers and laid plans for a revision of all the texts written at Boulder and Ann Arbor on the basis of the information obtained by classroom testing.

The Advisory Committee of SMSG had a busy year. One of the more interesting projects they undertook was a critical review of the textbooks written at Ann Arbor and Boulder. If it seems strange that the Advisory Committee of SMSG should review books written by the writing sessions of SMSG, it should be remembered that of the 27 members of the committee at the time, fewer than ten were involved in the writing sessions in other than a casual way. Furthermore, the members of the Advisory Committee represented a very wide cross section of the mathematical community, even as the writers had, and each felt an obligation to the colleagues he represented to see that their views were reflected in the work of the group. Therefore, the products of the writing sessions were given a thorough study by the committee, and a 12-page summary of their findings was compiled for the use of the revisers of the books. Not all members of the committee liked all the books, but neither had all the writers. The books were a synthesis of the thinking of many individuals, and the pages gave no hint of the enor-

Sample Books

mous amount of discussion, revision, and compromise that went into their writing. It is reasonably safe to say that almost all the critical questions raised by the Advisory Committee with respect to the finished products had also been raised during their writing and had been settled according to the will of the majority of the writers. The important point about the texts was not so much the treatment of any single topic, but the total picture they presented of an improved curriculum, and most of the Advisory Committee found the total picture. acceptable.

All meetings held by the Advisory Committee of SMSG have been conducted in essentially the same manner. Each meeting is presided over by the chairman, who is chosen each year by the committee. Professor Begle attends every meeting of this committee as an ex officio member, and also as Director of SMSG. This is the most important body in the SMSG organizational pattern, and the chief source to which Professor Begle can turn for counsel and advice. It contributes membership to all panels, and provides liaison with the most important professional organizations in the field of mathematics. Because of the diversity of interests and opinions represented by its membership, its meetings can never be described as dull. However, decisions arrived at by the committee are always arrived at by vote, so that whatever actions are taken by SMSG are always taken according to the will of the majority of the Advisory Committee. Because the Advisory Committee is also large, and because quick decisions are sometimes necessary in specific matters, an executive committee of five is elected to sit for the committee at such times. The Executive Committee can meet more frequently than the full committee, and can take care of routine or urgent matters.

The Advisory Committee met in April 1960 to consider the review of the textbooks. They also decided that SMSG should undertake the writing of an alternative book on geometry for the 10th grade. The book written by the 10th grade group at Boulder was, as has been noted, primarily a book on synthetic

SMSG: The Making of a Curriculum

geometry. The Commission on Mathematics had recommended that analytic geometry be started very early in the 10th year and then fused with synthetic geometry for the remainder of the course. The decision on the part of the 10th grade subgroup not to adopt this approach marked perhaps the greatest deviation from the Commission Report of any of the SMSG books, although, of course, minor differences of opinion were everywhere in evidence. In accord with this decision by the committee, Professor Begle agreed to initiate work along this line as soon as possible, but observed that no serious writing could be expected on the project before 1961.

The panel on monographs continued its efforts to secure manuscripts of mathematical monographs. During the year 1959–60, the editorial committee worked very hard to get into production the monographs it already had in progress. The editorial work necessary to process a manuscript proved to be more involved than had been anticipated. Though the writers of the monographs were all men of stature in the mathematical community, they were also men who habitually worked in the climate of advanced mathematics, and hence could not be expected to be overly familiar with the audience to which the monographs were addressed. To afford the authors some assistance in this area, each manuscript was reviewed by a number of high school teachers of mathematics, most of whom sought the opinions of some of their students. The results of these reviews, together with the suggestions of members of the editorial committee, were given to the authors to aid in the preparation of later drafts. SMSG made arrangements with Random House to publish commercial versions of the monographs for distribution to the public through the usual trade channels. The student editions were to be printed by Wesleyan University Press. By August 1960, the first six monographs were nearly ready to be sent to the printer.

Since writing sessions had already been held on the East Coast, in the Middle West, and in the Rocky Mountain area, it was felt appropriate to convene the 1960 session somewhere

Sample Books

on the Pacific Coast. After some preliminary exploration, Stanford University was selected as the site. Philip Heinecke of that institution was chosen to serve as business manager for the session, and would provide liaison between SMSG and the university. This session would involve slightly fewer people than had the Boulder-Ann Arbor sessions, but many new writers were needed. Staffing the teams to revise the books written at Ann Arbor and Boulder was not a serious problem, since many of the original writers had already agreed to aid in the revision. There would be four new projects, however. The elementary school material, the material for average students at both the junior and senior high school levels, and the alternative treatment of geometry would all have to be written by new people. After consulting with members of the Advisory Committee, the respective panels that were to supervise each project, and other prominent persons in the areas in which work was to be undertaken, Professor Begle was able to obtain the services of a new group of people eminently qualified for the work at hand.

A small group of psychologists would be meeting at Stanford during the summer. They would be evaluating data obtained from the administration of some psychological tests to a number of classes of elementary school pupils. The Conference on Elementary School Mathematics that was held in Chicago in February 1959 had made recommendations on psychological problems relevant to the teaching of mathematics. Though no panel had been appointed by Professor Begle to supervise work in this section, the Advisory Committee had indicated an interest in the matter, and some preliminary work had been going on since the middle of 1959. Professor Begle had formed an ad hoc committee of distinguished psychologists,[6] and they had outlined a plan for some needed research in this area. SMSG was particularly interested in evaluating the effectiveness of its new mathematics program in relation to children's attitudes, motives, anxieties, and skills. To narrow the

6. See Appendix, List 23.

SMSG: The Making of a Curriculum

field, the committee felt that it would be appropriate for SMSG to undertake a study of the possible application of psychology in (1) the development of intellectual capacities of children as they relate to mathematics, (2) learning theory, communication processes, etc., in relation to the teaching of mathematics, (3) the effects of nonintellective variables, such as values, attitudes, and motivation, on the learning of mathematics.

Under the sponsorship of SMSG, psychologists at Harvard, Yale, and the University of Maryland undertook some pilot studies. In particular, a psychological comparison of the SMSG 7th and 8th grade preliminary texts with some conventional texts was under way for the purpose of identifying some of the variables that would be involved in any such research. The writing session at Stanford would provide an opportunity for some additional work with psychological tests as well as an analysis of the test results obtained earlier.

To keep those interested in the activities of SMSG informed of all developments, two more newsletters were issued, one in September 1959, and another in March 1960. Furthermore, the number of speakers discussing SMSG at professional meetings increased sharply through this period. As a result of the wider awareness of the nature of SMSG and its aims, requests for textbooks for use in the fall semester of 1960 began to arrive at SMSG headquarters. Because the books would have to be revised before regular distribution could begin, it was for a while uncertain whether the public demand for the texts could be met. Subsequent negotiations with the printers made it feasible to release SMSG material for public use in the fall, subject to the understanding that the textbooks would be printed in two or three parts, and that only the first part of each text would be available at the beginning of the school year. The costs of the books to the school districts would be just the cost of printing and distribution. SMSG would receive no proceeds from such sales. Orders for books were required to be in SMSG's hands by June 15 to ensure delivery

Sample Books

of Part 1 by Labor Day. A small cross-sectional sample was made of school districts in the United States to try to anticipate the number of each volume to produce on the first printing.

Early in January 1960, the NSF extended the grant to Yale University for SMSG by an additional $1,700,000 to cover activities through the coming year. This brought the total of the SMSG grant (NSF–G–6308) to $3,000,000 for the period June 1958 to September 1960. To keep the National Science Foundation fully and continually informed with respect to the progress of the group, a monthly progress report was submitted, beginning in September 1959, which detailed SMSG activities. A copy of this report was sent to each member of the Advisory Committee.

The extension of the grant included funds for the Stanford writing session. This session opened at Stanford on June 27, 1960, with 87 participants, 14 fewer than at Boulder and Ann Arbor.[7] With the exception of some who wanted to rent homes of their own, they were housed in Branner Hall on the campus, just across the street from Trancos House where working space was provided. Housing policies were those usual to SMSG, namely, the calculated intermingling of high school and college people. Meals were provided in the Branner Hall dining room, and the usual recreational facilities were available for children.

The groups that had written the first set of SMSG sample textbooks at Boulder were now faced with a large amount of data in teacher questionnaires and test results from experimental centers. This had to be sorted, assimilated, and evaluated to provide a basis for revision. Because the work of revision was not to be as time-consuming as the original writing, each of the subgroups had been reduced appreciably in size, some to less than half of their original strength. The work of each subgroup in revising its own production will not be detailed here, since the procedures did not differ greatly from

7. See Appendix, List 24.

SMSG: The Making of a Curriculum

those used in the original writing, except that a much smaller amount of intragroup coordination, discussion, and general stress and strain was involved. Following an analysis of the data from the experimental centers, individuals or small teams began the revising. In some cases much rewriting was necessary while in others small changes were all that seemed indicated. By the close of the writing sessions, all the books had been modified in accordance with the experiences of the centers, and were ready for reproduction in revised form.

Of course, the 7th and 8th grade subgroup had the additional task of completing Volume II of their material in sequential form. The Volume II produced at Ann Arbor had consisted simply of various units to be classroom-tested, and had not been intended to serve as a sample textbook. This subgroup completed a new Volume II for the 8th grade that was a true sample textbook. It would be tried out in the schools and revised the following year.

There was one question that had to be settled on an intergroup basis, that of overlap of topics and consistency of symbolism and terminology. In the original writing of the books, one of the guiding principles had been that no prior association with certain new material (in particular, that having to do with sets) could be assumed at any level. Therefore, every sample textbook without exception had included a discussion of sets and set concepts at some point. It will be recalled that there had also been some overlap between the 11th and 12th grades in the area of trigonometry. Other areas of duplication appeared at various grade levels. To help deal with matters of duplication and consistency, Professor Begle appointed a coordinating committee consisting of the chairmen of the subgroups, and requested that they devote some specific attention to these problems, and also make provision for a special group to do nothing but work on exercises. This latter move was deemed necessary to ensure that each exercise set contain items at all levels of difficulty and that they be suitably graded. The coordinating committee held three meetings, one in May

Sample Books

prior to the opening of the writing session, and two more during the session. A standard symbolism was agreed upon and areas of overlap were identified. In each case, ways to eliminate the duplication were suggested. The revised editions of all the textbooks reflected the influence of this committee.

Of the new writing teams, perhaps the one with the most challenging task was that concerned with elementary school mathematics. While the other new projects could use the Boulder work as a point of departure, the elementary school project had to start from very close to scratch. Furthermore, their problems were legion. One of the difficulties facing all efforts at curriculum change was that of the training, or lack of training, of teachers. At the elementary level this problem was particularly serious. The actual mathematical training required of prospective elementary teachers by most colleges was slight almost to the vanishing point, and 29 states required no mathematics for certification of elementary school teachers. Therefore, the teacher's commentary produced by the group would have to be particularly detailed. A second difficulty was that too little was known about the extent to which children could learn mathematics beyond the rote learning of algorithms. Thus, the initial writing of the group would have to be largely of an exploratory nature.

To help provide a point of departure for the work of the elementary school group, the panel concerned with its supervision had adopted an organizational scheme somewhat different from that used by any of the previous groups. They designated, for the writing activities, a steering committee led by J. A. Cooley, of the University of Tennessee. This committee, in conjunction with the panel on elementary school mathematics, had the responsibility of drawing up outlines for suggested units before the session opened. This was done at a six-day meeting in March 1960. Thus, when the writing session opened, the participants had something with which to work. After a number of group sessions, the actual writing got under way. The group did not attempt to divide into grade-level

SMSG: The Making of a Curriculum

teams, because of the uncertainty surrounding the appropriate grade placement of many topics. Each teaching unit was prepared by a group of four or five people, some of whom were college teachers and some of whom were elementary school teachers or supervisors. When a first draft of a unit was completed, it was duplicated and circulated to all members of the group for criticism. Frequently, formal hearings were held on units in order to detail necessary revisions. When a draft satisfactory to the group was finally written, it was sent to the steering committee for further suggestions. If any changes appeared desirable, the committee then returned the manuscript to the original writing team for the necessary work; if no changes seemed necessary, the manuscript was edited and sent for final typing.

The content selected for experimentation was rich with topics new to the elementary school level. In addition to units on the traditional topics of arithmetic operations, fractional numbers, and the decimal system of numeration (these from the point of view of understanding principles as well as mastering computational algorithms), others were written dealing with set concepts, exponents, coordinates, and simple intuitive geometry. Some work had already been done on a local basis with some of this material, and, before beginning its own writing, the elementary school group carefully consulted such experimental treatments as could be obtained. Among others, the Universities of California, Illinois, Maryland, Minnesota, Syracuse, and Stanford had done pioneering work in this field.

The elementary school writing team had also been provided with two classes of summer school students with which to try out newly written units. The services of an experienced elementary school teacher were obtained, and, as each unit was completed, mimeographed copies were taken into the classroom and checked for teachability. The experiences of the teacher were then incorporated into a revised treatment, and also provided valuable suggestions for the teacher's commentary. Some of the finished units were tentatively organized into

Sample Books

a complete course for the 4th grade, and the rest were produced as miscellaneous units to be used in grades 5 and 6. The experimental centers, however, would be instructed to obtain data on some of the units at all three grade levels.

The pilot studies made by a few members of the panel on non-college-bound students had shown that it was worthwhile proceeding with a test on the assumption that average students could learn the same mathematics as the college-bound, provided it was presented slowly enough. Teams were on hand at Stanford to initiate the project. These teams were concerned with mathematics for the non-college-bound students (called the 9M group) and the average junior high school students (called the 7M group), and were committed to the use of the same general outlines as the earlier books written for the college-capable students at their respective levels.

Their tasks, therefore, were essentially to revise the material already written, but to do so with a different audience in mind. Such revisions, however, would entail a nearly complete rewriting of each course. The writers would have to concern themselves with a simpler vocabulary, breaking long sections of expository matter into smaller sections, and reworking the exercise sets to ensure an ample supply of items appropriate to the students who would be using the books. Also, more systematic use was to be made of chapter and cumulative reviews, which were felt to be very useful to such students. Various levels of abstraction were to be approached more slowly, although the general depth of treatment was not to be altered materially from that of the original work. Each team was to concern itself with texts to cover the work of two years.

Mildred Keiffer, Supervisor of Mathematics for the Cincinnati Public Schools, was appointed chairman of the 7M group. Having served earlier as a writer for the original 7th and 8th grade material, she could contribute valuable experience to the new work, both in writing procedures and point of view. There were nine members of this group, with the usual complement of both college and school personnel. Little time was

SMSG: The Making of a Curriculum

spent in original group discussion (their task was well-defined), and they settled to writing almost at once. The operating procedures of the group were essentially those used by the 7th and 8th grade group before them, which have been described in Chapter 4. There was one major difference, namely, that the writing was done individually rather than in teams of two. The reviewing procedures, however, were as stringent as ever, and frequent group hearings were held to criticize units. By the end of the session, this group had produced a volume in two parts covering most of the material from the original 7th grade book but with a slightly rearranged sequence and at a somewhat more leisurely pace. A third part, consisting of a few units from the 8th grade book, was also completed. All three parts would be classroom tested during the next academic year.

The 9M group was under the leadership of Walter Fleming, of Hamline University, and consisted of 12 persons. Although their specific task was writing a book for average students to parallel the 9th grade algebra book, the members of the group still felt it necessary to establish some kind of agreement on how to go about it. In particular, they wished to establish the level of difficulty they were to approximate. This consideration and the necessity of thoroughly familiarizing themselves with the exact nature of the book written by the previous 9th grade group (which was even then under revision) consumed two weeks before the actual writing began. When they started, they used a writing procedure similar to that employed by their predecessors at the 9th grade level.

First drafts were written by various persons, but two or three writers prepared all final drafts. Though no official editorial panel existed, Professor Fleming reviewed each chapter before it went to the typist. This group employed full-group hearings on every first draft. A special exercise-writing team was established, and the exercises for each chapter were prepared as soon as first drafts of the expository material were completed. In general, the teacher's-commentary material for

Sample Books

each chapter was prepared by the writer of the chapter. When the writing session was over, this group had completed a treatment of the material included in the first half of the 9th grade book for the college-capable students, designed to be taught over a period of one year. The length of time to be spent on each topic was roughly doubled.

The preliminary edition of their book contained some features not found in the other 9th grade book. For example, they provided oral exercises to precede most of the problem sets; they introduced certain variations in format for the purpose of arresting the student's attention; they included, prior to each exercise set, a few questions designed to lead to oral discussions in class, questions that gave the student an opportunity to check his understanding of the explanatory portion of the section. Every chapter was followed by a chapter review, and cumulative reviews were inserted at frequent intervals. In brief, the writers had made an effort to lower the voltage of the material in any way they could.

The number of typists hired for the Stanford writing session rose to 18, the experiences of the preceding writing sessions having demonstrated the necessity for a veritable battalion of such help. Also, the services of two expert draftsmen were again necessary. The reduction of the number of participants in the revising teams for the books for grades 7 through 12 created some unforeseen difficulties in proofreading and in problem solutions for teacher's commentaries. The writers were much too busy to be able to handle these items. SMSG sought and obtained the services of a number of highly competent high school teachers from the area to handle these matters. Since the Palo Alto School District had participated in the classroom testing the previous year, they had a sizeable group of teachers already familiar with SMSG material upon which the writing session could draw for this help. Four experts on tests were present at the session for the purpose of providing counsel on exercise sets, and for writing sample questions for tests to be included in the revised teacher's commentaries. The work done by three of these experts the preceding year at Boulder at two grade levels had drawn favorable comment from the teachers in the experimental centers, and it was felt that such items would be of value at other grade levels as well.

The Stanford writing session, then, followed much the same pattern as had the Boulder and Ann Arbor sessions the previous year. Indeed, the pattern of SMSG writing sessions was essentially set by the 1959 experiences, and would show little variation in subsequent years. Though many new writers would attend each session, there would always be a sufficient carry-over of people working on revisions or other continuing projects to maintain a continuity of the spirit and sense of purpose that characterized the work of the group in its formative period. August 1960 marked the completion of the first large-scale SMSG project, the sample textbooks for the college-capable category of students. It also marked the beginning of a period in which, it was hoped, the work of SMSG would have an impact on the commercial textbooks used in the United States, and hence on mathematics education in our schools.

6 From Yale to Stanford

After the close of the Stanford writing session in August 1960, the usual blizzard of manuscripts descended upon the headquarters of SMSG at Yale. Royce Hargrove, Coordinator of Science and Mathematics for the Corpus Christi Public Schools of Corpus Christi, Texas, was added to the headquarters staff for the period extending from September 1, 1961, through January 31, 1961, to help deal with the preparation of manuscripts for printers. The services of Mr. Wagner as assistant to Professor Begle were also secured for an additional year.

The production and distribution of sample textbooks involved two different kinds of publication during the 1960–61 period. First, there were the materials in their preliminary form. As before, these had to be printed and distributed to the experimental centers. In this category were the 8th grade textbook, the 7M and 9M courses, and the elementary school units. The second kind of publication with which SMSG was concerned included the revised editions of the sample textbooks for grades 7 and 9–12. These were considered finished, and would be available for public sale. As explained in the preceding chapter, a sample had been taken of the number of textbooks that would probably be required to meet the demands of interested school districts. The results of this sample were projected into an estimate of the number of copies to be

SMSG: The Making of a Curriculum

involved in the first printing, and orders were placed with printers. Because orders were still arriving in quantity at the time of the deadline for ordering, June 15, the deadline was extended into July, with delivery of the first part of each volume due near Labor Day.

It was clear from the magnitude of sales during this period —about 130,000 books during the 1960–61 academic year—that SMSG would have to divest itself of the task of distributing the books, since it had neither the inclination nor the facilities to cope with the problems involved. Furthermore, the texts were not to be marketed over any lengthy period of time. It had been decided very early that as soon as commercial textbooks of comparable quality were placed on sale, SMSG would remove its books from the market, and thus the difficulty and expense of establishing a department for handling the revised textbooks would not be warranted.

Individual purchases of revised SMSG textbooks could not be made until well into the spring of 1961. The demands made on the available supply by schools, as well as the distribution problem presented by the production of each book in separate parts, rendered it inadvisable to make sales to individuals until after the last part of each volume was printed. At that time, individual sets (a "set" in this case meaning all parts of one volume) could be sold to anyone who wanted them.

Late in the spring, the Yale University Press was given the exclusive rights to print, advertise, and sell all of the then existent SMSG revised textbooks. Since this press was also a nonprofit organization, the books would still be available to the public at cost. Furthermore, the Yale Press agreed to reduce the physical dimensions of the texts from the notebook-sized volumes of the preliminary edition to a more easily managed 7"x10" package and, in the process, was able to reduce substantially the cost of each volume. By May, all the necessary paper work had been completed, and the headquarters staff of SMSG felt relieved to be free of the burden of processing orders. As will be seen, the relief was only temporary.

From Yale to Stanford

There were other aspects of the public distribution of SMSG texts that had to be examined. While SMSG was to produce texts for sale only until such time as commercial publishers could offer books of like nature, the question of when such books would be available had to be examined. That is, how was SMSG to determine when it should cease the sale of its own products for use in the schools? At first it had seemed that an arbitrary period of five years would serve the purpose, and that after any revised text had been available for this period it would automatically be withdrawn from sale. Later meetings of the Advisory Committee, however, found the feelings of the members somewhat changed. It was proposed that a review committee be established each year and any withdrawal of SMSG textbooks be based upon the findings of this committee. This provided a means of assuring school districts that were using SMSG material of a continuing source of supply, and would not leave them without textbooks should comparable books fail to appear within five years.

SMSG continued to distribute the books for experimental centers. The year 1960–61 found some 15,000 students using preliminary versions of SMSG textbooks in centers about the country, as well as several thousand more in points (see page 87). Evaluation questionnaires detailing the experiences of the teachers involved flowed into Yale in a steady stream.

The NSF grant to SMSG was extended by an additional $1,184,200 for the period September 1960 to September 1961, raising the total grant to above $4,000,000. Included as an item in this grant extension was a fund for an evaluation study to determine the short-term effects of the use of SMSG materials on students. The genesis of this study was an interesting one, and dealt with a commonplace in the history of the mathematics curriculum. The relative importance of mathematical skills (the ability to perform routine manipulations) and mathematical concepts (the mathematical rationale for the manipulations) had been debated for a very long period of time, much longer, in fact, than had the question of modernizing the curriculum. Those with a utilitarian viewpoint generally insisted that the most important thing for students was an ability to perfom routine calculations in a rapid and accurate manner, and that while an understanding of the theory underlying the calculations would be all to the good, it was no more necessary to the student than was a knowledge of the theory of the internal combustion engine to the driver of an automobile. Persons holding this viewpoint generally tended to rate the efficacy of an instructional unit in mathematics on the basis of how well the student performed on some sort of standardized test in arithmetic processes upon completion of the unit. They were interested in skills.

On the other side of this argument were those who felt that an understanding of the logical structure underlying any use of numbers was of extreme importance. They believed that an understanding of the nature of mathematics, which, in their view, was not at all discernible in a course in the manipulation of symbols, was needed by every educated person in the twentieth century, and indispensable for any who hoped to engage in work in scientific or technical fields. While they believed that skills were useful, they felt that there was more to mathematics than manipulations. It was their opinion that many of the difficulties encountered by students in their college courses in physics, engineering, chemistry, and the like could be directly traced to the overemphasis in high school mathematics on computational and manipulative procedures to the everlasting detriment of the student's ability to use logical inference in any kind of situation whatsoever. The ability to *apply* mathematics to physical situations seemed to them strongly dependent upon the student's understanding of mathematics itself as the embodiment of logical reasoning.

The SMSG writers had felt that both skills and concepts were important. Because their books did reflect a great deal of emphasis in the area of logical inference and logical structure, however, they were sensitive to the beliefs of some that the manipulative skills of students using SMSG materials

From Yale to Stanford

might suffer. Accordingly, they felt it appropriate, once the revised textbooks were available, to test the hypothesis that students using SMSG materials would suffer no loss in their ability to perform routine manipulative computations. To undertake this test, they engaged the services of the Educational Testing Service (the publishers of the College Entrance Examination Board Examinations, as well as of other widely respected tests) to perform a one-year experiment using SMSG materials. The experiment was to test the aforementioned hypothesis as well as the achievement, in SMSG mathematics, of students who had studied in both SMSG and traditional classes. The experimental design and story of the testing program is available in SMSG's *Newsletter 10,* November 1961, and will not be related here. The results of the experiment, however, are relevant. The findings were that SMSG students suffered no statistically significant loss in skills over a period of a year. Moreover, they did show a statistically significant superiority over other students in understanding the subject matter of SMSG materials. While the latter finding is natural enough, the former was a substantiation of the hypothesis that prompted the experiment.

An interesting result of the publication of these findings was a brief spate of criticism to the effect that as long as SMSG students did no better than those in traditional classes in this experiment, there seemed no reason for changing the status quo. Such criticism missed the whole point. It had never been the contention of SMSG that its material would, over the short term, materially improve the students' ability in computation or manipulation. The tests used in the evaluation had been revised and refined for many years specifically to determine how well students in traditional courses could do traditional things. To expect that, in a year's time, a set of textbooks designed for wholly different purposes should produce an improvement in manipulatory skills over textbooks that specialized in such things was unreasonable. The fact that the experiment showed no loss in such skills was surprising in itself, since the hypothesis tested was based on little more than a tentative philosophical conjecture. The experiment did show that considerably more evaluation of experimental curricula, and in particular of SMSG materials, was required. Though the short-term results were satisfactory, the long-term results, which the writers for SMSG felt were of immensely greater importance, remained to be determined.

Another extensive set of experiments using SMSG materials was conducted by the Minnesota National Laboratory for the Improvement of Secondary Mathematics, under the direction of Paul C. Rosenbloom, of the Department of Mathematics, Institute of Technology, University of Minnesota. SMSG had worked closely with this laboratory, whose function was that of performing scientific experimentation and evaluation for SMSG since the laboratory's official organization in 1959. Part of the financial support of the laboratory was borne by SMSG, and part by the State of Minnesota.

The experiments conducted by this laboratory ranged in grade level from the kindergarten through high school, and encompassed students with all degrees of mathematical ability. As one example, the laboratory adapted the 9th and 10th grade SMSG texts for use in correspondence courses for able students. For additional information on the functions and operations of this laboratory, the reader is referred to the SMSG newsletters, in particular *Newsletter 2* and *Newsletter 10*.

When SMSG came into being in March 1958, it was not clear how long it would take to reach its objectives. By early 1961, its experiences had made it clear that the general kinds of activities it had undertaken—especially the close collaboration between classroom teachers, supervisors, educational specialists, and research mathematicians—ought to be continued indefinitely. The completion of the sample-textbook series gave evidence of the value of such collaboration, and during their writing the need for several new projects had developed.

In view of the clear need for a continuation of the work begun by SMSG, a conference was held in Chicago in February

From Yale to Stanford

1961 to consider ways of sustaining the momentum already generated. The sixty participants at the conference represented all parts of the country and the mathematical profession.[1] The chief recommendation resulting from the two-day conference was that SMSG should continue indefinitely, carrying on with its existing programs but broadening its scope to provide assistance in all areas of school mathematics education. It was further recommended that the Advisory Committee be given a more formal structure and that some of its members be named by the Conference Board of the Mathematical Sciences, a group that represents all the major mathematical organizations in the United States. These recommendations were transmitted to the SMSG Advisory Committee for its consideration. At a meeting of this body on May 13, 1961, a committee was appointed to draw up a set of bylaws that would implement the recommendations of the conference.

During the academic year 1960–61, the volume of work of the panel on monographs increased sharply, and the panel requested that its membership be assigned on a rotating basis. Many proposals for monographs had to be screened and evaluated. In addition, monographs in progress had to be read and criticized by the members. In view of the pressing demands made upon them by their regular duties, the members of the panel felt that a third of their membership should be changed each year, and this request was honored by the Advisory Committee.

The panel had six monographs on the verge of publication. By June 1961, three of them were bound and complete, but were not immediately released for sale. The panel had decided that their initial venture into the market should be made with six books, and the release of any one of the books was delayed pending completion of them all. The Wesleyan University Press, which had been interested in publishing the student editions of the monographs, found that it could not proceed with the project, and SMSG elected to produce the first six

1. See Appendix, List 25.

SMSG: The Making of a Curriculum

volumes itself. While Random House would publish a trade version of the monographs, SMSG would offer a more economical version for school use to sell for about half the trade price. The editorial committee of the panel was exceedingly busy during this academic year, and the technical editor, Anneli Lax, of New York University, devoted full time to directing the production of the books.

It will be recalled that the Advisory Committee had, in April 1960, recommended that an alternative geometry be written, paralleling the recommendations of the Commission on Mathematics somewhat more closely than the first SMSG version. Because of the short time between April and June, the writing of the book was put off until the writing session of 1961. It was therefore necessary, during the academic year 1960-61, for Professor Begle to secure a new group of writers for this book. The volume would be produced under the auspices of the panel on sample textbooks. R. A. Rosenbaum of Wesleyan University agreed to serve as chairman for the team. A five-day planning session was held at Princeton University, March 27-31, to outline the proposed book and to organize the coming writing session. Eleven of the fifteen members of the writing team were present, as well as two members of the Commission on Mathematics.[2] At the end of the five days, a complete outline for the book had been agreed upon, an outline that included the postulate system to be employed. In addition, some preliminary writing had been done on a few of the chapters. Between the close of the planning session and the beginning of the 1961 writing session, copies of the work of this planning group were circulated to many former SMSG writers for comment. To continue close liaison with the panel on sample textbooks during the developmental period of this project, Professor Rosenbaum was added to the panel.

The panel on 7th and 8th grades, with still one 8th grade volume to revise, had substantially completed its allotted task and held no more formal meetings. The panel on teacher

2. See Appendix, List 26.

From Yale to Stanford

training met once, in January 1961, to review the progress of the study guides and the translations from foreign languages that were proceeding under their direction. The third volume in the Studies in Mathematics series, that written by Professor Vincent Haag and entitled *Structure of Elementary Algebra,* was placed on sale in July 1960, and at the same time a fourth volume, *Geometry,* by B. V. Kutuzov, was released. This latter volume had been translated from the Russian and was considered a good source of supplementary material for teachers. In November of the same year, the fifth volume was published: *Concepts of Informal Geometry,* by Richard D. Anderson, of Louisiana State University. In July 1961, Volumes 6 and 8 were produced, followed shortly by Volume 7. These were materials especially adapted from earlier SMSG writings (grades 7, 8, and 9) of particular interest and value to elementary school teachers. Thus, by the fall of 1961, SMSG had produced eight separate volumes for use by teachers from elementary school through the 12th grade level.

The panel on non-college-bound students found itself with a new name during this period, a name more descriptive of its actual concerns. It became the panel on underdeveloped mathematical talent, under which title it continued the work it had been doing, namely, attempting to develop unused mathematical potential in the average student. This panel met twice during the academic year 1960-61, once on March 4 in New York City, and again on June 24 at Yale, just prior to the opening of the 1961 writing session. Both meetings dealt with the 7M and 9M textbooks then being tried out in the schools. Plans were laid for the revision of those parts of the sample textbooks already completed as well as for the completion of the material originally proposed.

The panel on elementary school mathematics held two meetings during the 1960-61 period, one in Chicago in February and another at Yale two days prior to the opening of the 1961 writing session. Both meetings were concerned with reviewing reports on work underway as well as planning for the work

SMSG: The Making of a Curriculum

of the next writing session. One question with which they had to grapple was that of format. The SMSG elementary school units written at Stanford were designed to be consumable—that is, the students could write directly in the booklets. It soon became apparent, however, that with the number of students involved, to say nothing of the large number of units written, the expense involved in producing materials of this type would be large—in fact, prohibitive to many school districts. Professor Begle therefore asked the panel to consider a redesigned package, one that would not be consumable.

While the panel was reluctant to dispense with a format that was perhaps pedagogically superior, it nevertheless agreed to explore an alternative design that would not be so expensive to use in everyday situations. One of the tasks of the coming writing session, therefore, would be to develop a format for nonconsumable materials. The panel also discussed the extension of work downward to the kindergarten, but elected to postpone any action in this area until the next academic year, at which time specific plans could be formulated.

The steadily increasing scope of the activities of SMSG had made it necessary for Professor Begle to remain on full-time duty with the Group during the year 1960–61, and Yale University had agreed to extend his leave of absence for this additional period. Both Professor Begle and Dr. Wagner were called upon to make frequent trips to various parts of the United States to check on SMSG activities in progress and to address meetings of local and national professional organizations. In addition, Professor Begle attended all meetings of panels as well as all Advisory Board meetings, and these almost invariably necessitated travel. Whenever possible, panel meetings were scheduled to meet either immediately prior to or subsequent to other meetings—for example, those of the Advisory Board or those of a conference. Barring this possibility, two or more panels or committees might be scheduled to meet consecutively.

Another challenge for the headquarters staff developed dur-

From Yale to Stanford

ing the academic year 1961–62 when Professor Begle accepted an appointment to the faculty of Stanford University. In the interests of having SMSG continue to function at the same level of effectiveness, Yale, Stanford, and the NSF decided it was imperative that SMSG headquarters be moved to Stanford. This necessitated, through the late spring and early summer, some careful planning, as well as the packing of the headquarters' files. Professor Begle, during one of his trips to the West Coast, made an intensive search for replacements for the vacancies on the headquarters staff that would result from the move. The results of his search were eminently satisfactory. Dr. Wagner, who was leaving SMSG to accept an appointment to the faculty of Michigan State University, would be replaced by George Roehr, Consultant in Mathematics for the California State Department of Education. Mr. Roehr was an experienced administrator and widely known in California educational circles. The position of administrative assistant, held by Mrs. Phyllis Stevens, would not be filled. Instead, her duties would be taken over by two new employees. In addition, Professor Begle acquired a new secretary, Mrs. Ella Elliott, who, by virtue of an extensive prior association with Stanford University, could offer valuable assistance to the Group during the period of establishing new headquarters.

The headquarters staff also had to plan the 1961 writing session. The West Coast having been the location of the previous year's session, and with the move to Stanford being planned for late August and early September, it was felt advisable to gather the writers on the Yale University campus again. The necessary arrangements were made with the university. Personnel requirements were surveyed, and a temporary typing staff of eighteen was obtained. The writing session participants would largely be those from the preceding year's session at Stanford. In addition to the new members of the alternative geometry team, however, a few additions were made to other groups.

The fourth writing session of SMSG opened in New Haven

SMSG: The Making of a Curriculum

on June 26, 1961, with 71 participants.[3] The group was housed in Branford College, but dining facilities and some of the working area lay in Saybrook College, just across a small courtyard. The writing groups included a team for the new geometry with coordinates, the 8th grade revising team, revising teams for 7M and 9M, and the elementary school team. This session did not differ materially from its predecessors except that, by this time, the headquarters staff was wise in the ways of writing sessions, and the pre-planning had managed to anticipate almost all possible points of difficulty. Since there was a considerable carry-over of participants from the previous session at Stanford (there were only 29 new faces) the participants meshed with the smoothness of experience, and the work of each group began almost at once.

The one completely new writing team, that of the alternative geometry book, began its operation in much the same way that the elementary group had begun the previous year. They were in possession of a rather complete outline (the work of the earlier planning session) and hence did not have to start from scratch. The steering committee for this group had met in Middletown, Connecticut, one week prior to the opening of the writing session, and made preliminary assignments of responsibility. They had also agreed upon a tentative time schedule for each section of the proposed book. The working procedures for this geometry-with-coordinates group (or GW group as it will hereafter be designated) were relatively informal. In addition to the steering committee, whose function was largely that of pre-planning, they designated writing teams, a rewrite team, an exercise team, and a teacher's-commentary team. The rewrite team was asked to do all second drafts, but, as it soon developed, this proved impractical, and this team was absorbed into the general writing.

As each writing team completed a draft it was duplicated and distributed, and the customary group meetings were held to review the material. Following the demise of the rewrite

[3] See Appendix, List 27.

From Yale to Stanford

team, each writing group generally undertook the production of its own revised drafts, although new teams would occasionally try to produce an improved version. All final drafts were processed by an editor and by Professor Rosenbaum, and were then sent on to the typists. One member of the GW group was designated to serve as production manager, and was responsible for the coordination of all work. The exercise-writing team and the teacher's-commentary team were, of course, performing the functions indicated by their titles, although other writers supplemented the work of both teams.

By the close of the session, the GW group had completed a preliminary version of both a textbook and a teacher's commentary. The geometry courses incorporated in their product differed from the first SMSG geometry course in many ways. Though the basic postulate system employed was substantially the same as the original one, much more emphasis was given to one-dimensional coordinate geometry in the early part of the new book, and, once the Pythagorean theorem was established, coordinate or synthetic proofs were used as best suited each situation. In addition, the student was introduced to vectors and vector techniques. Generally speaking, this alternative treatment paralleled the recommendations of the Commission on Mathematics to a much greater extent than did the first SMSG geometry textbook.

The 7th and 8th grade group, reduced this year to seven writers, was concerned with a revised edition of the SMSG 8th grade textbook. Since much of the material in the book had been tested in classrooms for two years, the revision was made quite rapidly. The group finished its job in July, before the close of the writing session.

The 7M group of 13 persons was faced with the necessity of revising the 7th grade material written the preceding year, and the 8th grade text. In accord with the experiences of other groups, they found the reports from the classroom teachers who had tested the material to be very helpful. In the light of these, the first two parts of the three written at Stanford

117

were revised, while at the same time a new fourth part was written. Unlike the preceding three parts, which had been taken entirely from the original 7th grade text, part four included selected topics from the 8th grade level. By the close of the writing session, this group had a new sequence in four parts for the average student in junior high school, and these would all be classroom-tested during the 1961–62 academic year.

The 9M group was also concerned with both the revision of existing material and the creation of new. Their efforts at Stanford had resulted in a revised treatment of approximately half of the original 9th grade algebra textbook, together with a few selected topics from the second half. This year they had the classroom teacher's comments to aid in the revision of this material. There were 11 members of the group in 1961 as opposed to 12 in 1960, and their operating procedures were little changed from those of the preceding year. The end of the writing session found them with a complete treatment of the original SMSG 9th grade text, but one that was planned for use over a two-year span. The material was to be bound in four parts, and classroom-tested in the fall.

The elementary school writing team had the question of a new format before them, as well as the job of revising the content of their units in the light of classroom experience. The group had been augmented during the year, and, instead of the 17 writers present at Stanford, they now numbered 24. The writing procedures used during the session at Stanford had proved satisfactory for the group and were retained during this session. The results of the 1961 writing session included a complete revision of the 4th grade sequence, a complete 5th grade sequence, and all but five chapters of a 6th grade sequence. The isolated units of the preceding year had been revised and merged into a continuous program for grades 4, 5, and 6. The format was of a nonconsumable type, although the material was still bound in individual units to facilitate classroom use. The teacher's commentaries, which were charac-

From Yale to Stanford

terized by detailed suggestions for classroom presentations, were also bound individually.

These books presented to the mathematical community a program that differed from the traditional even more extensively than the high school books had. To begin with, the black and white typewritten pages and the sparsity of pictures was utterly alien to traditional books at this level. This was, however, the result of necessity, not choice, and such features would no doubt have been included had it been possible. Still, they were features of the books.

A more important difference lay in the mathematical caliber of the content. Though all of the familiar algorithms of arithemetic were included, the writers had made a herculean effort to base them on sound mathematical principles and not only to teach the students how to do something but also to make sure they understood what they were doing and why they were doing it. The vocabulary used was, in the opinions of the SMSG elementary school teachers and supervisors, appropriate for the students at the levels concerned. Nevertheless, the text contained a number of words heretofore eschewed by comparable books. For example, the book for grade 5 used such phrases as "polygonal region," "congruent figures," "intersection of sets," and many others. The philosophy behind such use was that the words themselves were no lengthier than many words already familiar to the students, the concepts involved were highly intuitive, and it was a sound educational tenet not to teach what would have to be unlearned later.

The problems posed by the terminology might very well prove a greater obstacle to the teachers than to the students, because the teachers had been long accustomed to using popular euphemisms for many of the words, while the students had not. The problem sets in the texts were carefully constructed, and ranged in type from simple drill exercises to relatively difficult items, called "braintwisters," which would challenge the very best students. Heavy use was made of sections titled "Explorations," wherein the children were led naturally into

SMSG: The Making of a Curriculum

the discovery of significant questions and thus into interest in finding answers to the questions. These sections paved the way for the work that followed. The topics new to these grade levels included a consideration of prime numbers, sets, geometry, number bases, and number sentences, among others. Since certain of these topics were also covered in the 7th grade text, the problem of repetition again reared its head, but this will be discussed again later.

Another new project that began at the 1961 writing session was that on programed learning. Programed learning was a relatively new concept evolving from the work of stimulus-response psychologists, chiefly B. F. Skinner, of Harvard University. In this method of learning, students proceed through new material in very small steps. Information is given to the student in sequential bits, each bit requiring some form of overt response by the student, writing something, pushing a button, pulling a lever, or some other activity. Having made a response, the student is immediately informed as to whether the response is correct. In theory, immediately informing the student that he has made a correct response (the bits of information are presented so as to minimize incorrect responses) provides a reinforcement of the response, and helps the student retain the information given him. Alternative forms exist for the presentation of information to the student, and more than one rationale is proposed for the construction of programs. N. A. Crowder, of U. S. Industries, Incorporated, developed a branching type of presentation called an intrinsic program, in which the student and program interact. The program contains a number of different paths or branches by which the student may acquire a desired level of knowledge in a particular topic, and progress through the program depends upon the responses made by the student. In a Crowder program, the student selects one of a number of multiple choices, and is sent on in the program in accord with the choice he makes.

The use of programed materials in schools had been steadily increasing over the few years prior to 1961. It is true that most of the work was highly experimental, but some commercial ventures were being made in this direction, and the role of teaching machines and other devices using the programing concept was the subject of a great deal of interest and discussion in the professional literature. SMSG was early aware of the potential uses of this instructional medium, but during the first years of its existence could find no opportunity to look into it in any detail. The Chicago Conference on Future Responsibilities for School Mathematics, however, had specifically requested that SMSG prepare and test mathematical programs. The Advisory Committee agreed that a careful study of programed learning should be undertaken, and appointed an ad hoc committee to advise the Director on procedures to be followed. The report of the ad hoc committee was presented at the Advisory Committee meeting of May 13, and was approved in principle by the group. The report recommended that the 9th grade algebra course would probably be the most useful to program, and that this should be done in both Skinner and Crowder formats. It also presented a number of suggestions relative to the use to be made of the programs and asserted that their preparation should be supervised by a committee including both mathematicians and psychologists.

As a result of this report, Professor Begle appointed a panel on programed learning to supervise a project designed to investigate several aspects of programed instruction.[4] The first meeting of this panel was held on June 16, 1961, at Harvard University, and concerned itself with the recommendations of the ad hoc committee on programed learning. In particular, the panel decided that a comparison of the relative effectiveness of the Skinner (linear) type program, the Crowder (branching) type program, and a regular SMSG text might be a worthwhile first step.

Because the acquisition of meaningful data from such a comparison required that the experiment be carefully de-

4. See Appendix, List 28.

SMSG: The Making of a Curriculum

signed and conducted, Leander Smith, of Westwood, Massachusetts, was added to the headquarters staff of SMSG as full-time coordinator for the program.

His first two tasks were to complete a detailed design for the experiment, and to write a manual that could be used to train programers for the writing. The committee in charge of the study had suggested that it would be better to train mathematics personnel to program rather than train programers in mathematics. While the manual was being written, another group of mathematicians who had been associated with the writing of the 9th grade text were preparing a detailed statement of the specific teaching objectives of each section in the book. This was to be used by the programers.

To expedite the writing and preliminary testing of the program, a "center" plan was adopted. Each center would be responsible for either a linear program or branching program, covering a given section or sections of the text, and all of them would feed material back through SMSG headquarters for duplicating and field testing. It was hoped that this arrangement, in conjunction with a summer writing session in 1962, would make it possible for the full-scale experiment to be undertaken in the 1962–63 school year.

Once the manual for programers was written and the list of objectives compiled, the training of programers could begin. Therefore, on August 7, 1961, twelve persons with mathematical backgrounds were selected from a list previously drawn up by Professor Begle, and brought to the Yale writing session for initial training in programing. During their two-week stay at Yale, they examined existing algebra programs, carefully studied the manual written by Mr. Smith, and wrote and criticized short sequences of frames using SMSG material. After their wishes in the matter were determined, the writers were separated into two teams of six, one team to work on linear programing and the other on the branching type. When they returned to their homes, each writer was to become a center chairman and was, in turn, to train others in his center.

From Yale to Stanford

With the close of the writing session in August 1961, SMSG could look back on a very busy and productive year. Five newsletters had been written and distributed during the period in an effort to keep the public apprised of the work of the Group. With the appointment of a committee to establish bylaws for a more formal organizational structure, Professor Begle had set in motion a series of actions designed to make SMSG a useful, contributing agency to serve the interests of the American mathematical community for many years to come. As SMSG headquarters turned toward the West Coast, it was with the knowledge that the Group was beginning a new phase in its existence.

7 Reorganization

When SMSG moved its headquarters from New Haven, Connecticut, to Palo Alto, California, it did not transfer all its operations. The literature that had been distributed during the preceding year listed the Yale address as the source from which to order books, and it was feared that if this were abruptly changed, monumental confusion would ensue. As it developed, monumental confusion ensued anyway, but not because of the move. The sale of revised editions of the SMSG textbooks had, during the 1960–61 school year, amounted to some 130,000 volumes. On the basis of this, and considering the amount of advertising undertaken by the Yale Press with respect to its acquisition of the distribution rights for SMSG textbooks, a substantial increase was planned in the first Yale Press printing. Before the end of June 1961, both SMSG and the Yale Press became uncomfortably aware that there had been a serious underestimation of the demand. By July 1, orders had been received for 226,000 books, and an order was rushed through for a second printing. Before the opening of school for the fall semester, orders for an additional 100,000 books were on hand. This extraordinary increase in interest over the previous year had not been anticipated and strained the printing and distribution facilities beyond their immediate ability to respond. While the Yale Press was frantically working to print additional material and was seeking new

Reorganization

avenues for distribution, the opening day of school arrived in many districts around the nation. With stricken resignation, the office staffs of both SMSG and the Press contemplated telephone switchboards in full bloom. To the question, "Where are our books?" an appropriate response was sought. Every errant shipment was traced from the receipt of the order through all of the organizational channels until it was located, and was then expedited to whatever extent possible. Not all of the difficulty, however, could be ascribed to the erroneous assessment of demand. Many orders for books were received couched in such terms as "Send 25 copies of the SMSG mathematics book," or "Send 50 copies of the blue book." Since there existed, at the time, something on the order of 35 or 40 different SMSG mathematics publications, and since all of the preliminary editions printed in 1959 were in blue covers (and, in any event, were not for classroom use) nothing could be done with such orders except to return them for clarification. This, of course, resulted in quite a large loss of time in securing the desired books.

It was early October before the printing and distribution crises were resolved, and, in the meantime, orders for another 50,000 volumes had arrived. The academic year 1961–62 found the total sales of SMSG texts approaching 500,000 volumes. Since these volumes pertained only to grade levels 7 to 12, and since the total United States enrollment in these grades was in excess of 10 million, not more than 5 per cent of the students in the country were using SMSG materials. Still, considering the physical characteristics of the books (paper covers, no color, no illustrations), it seemed evident that private publishers could find a ready market for professionally produced materials of like content. In view of the formidable production and distribution problems involved in the continued sale of these sample texts, SMSG eagerly looked forward to the introduction of satisfactory commercial replacements for them.

The portion of the SMSG operations still remaining at Yale was primarily concerned with the distribution of the

SMSG: The Making of a Curriculum

Studies in Mathematics, Conference Reports (the proceedings of each SMSG-sponsored conference were printed, bound, and available to anyone interested), Study Guides, Supplementary Units, and the monographs of the New Mathematical Library. The close similarity of the addresses for ordering materials from the Yale Press and from SMSG led to some additional confusion. Orders for materials handled by Yale Press were frequently addressed to SMSG, and vice versa. Though in all such cases the orders were immediately forwarded to the proper place, some slight delay was incurred in the process. It cannot be said, however, that this delay was of significance, except when it occurred in conjunction with other delays of a similar nature. These might include such things as ordering a book by both number and title where these did not agree, improperly filled out purchase orders, or failure to specify where the books were to be shipped. The cumulative effect of a number of such discrepancies would understandably be a late delivery. Another task being assumed by the Yale branch of SMSG was the typing, for reproduction, of the work done at the writing session. This typing, as usual, extended into December, with each separate part being sent to the printer as it was completed.

While the Yale segment of SMSG was typing manuscripts and fighting the battle of the textbook sales, the main headquarters was busily engaged in establishing itself in a new environment. Pending the construction of a new building in which they were to be allotted space, the headquarters staff was temporarily housed in somewhat cramped quarters in the Cubberley Education Building at Stanford, but by late October had moved into the newly finished Cedar Hall. Although the unpacking and rearranging of the newly arrived files of SMSG was a tedious and time-consuming chore, it had one saving aspect. The staff had an opportunity to cull inactive items from the mass of documents and thus begin life at Stanford with a new, streamlined set of files. A dead-item file was established in a storage area separate from headquarters, and

Reorganization

this helped somewhat to alleviate the space problem that seemed always to be with them.

During all the upheaval that accompanied the move to Stanford, the activities of SMSG went on as usual. The testing centers had to be supplied with materials, and their incoming reports had to be processed.[1] In addition to the centers, fifty-two points were in operation. This year, for the first time, another experimental arrangement was established, a "paying point." Because the number of school districts requesting an opportunity to be considered "centers" or "points" for SMSG preliminary materials far exceeded the funds that SMSG had available for this purpose, paying points were established. A paying point was required to pay for all materials and consulting services required, and to submit the usual completed questionnaires on classroom results obtained by using the material. This served the mutually satisfactory purpose of the school districts' obtaining the books they wanted, while SMSG obtained the information it needed to revise the material. As it developed, the year 1961–62 saw more paying points (88) in existence than centers and points combined. In consequence, the summer writing session in 1962 would be in possession of a larger number of completed questionnaires per volume than any previous session. The distribution of books for centers posed few difficulties, since the plans for all testing of material were laid well in advance.

The academic year 1961–62 also saw what was largely a second testing of the elementary school, 7M, and 9M materials, and hence only the personnel of the new geometry-with-coordinates test centers were involved in the customary orientation conference. This was held in Chicago on September 23, 1961.[2] Because the elementary school writing groups had not finished a final draft of the last part of the grade-six book, the panel and steering committee for elementary school mathematics held a three-day meeting, also in Chicago, to complete the manu-

1. See Appendix, List 29.
2. See Appendix, List 30.

127

script on this project. On October 8, the remaining portions of the book were dispatched to Yale for typing.

The ad hoc committee of the Advisory Committee, appointed to draw up bylaws reorganizing SMSG, made its report to the full committee on October 14, 1961.[3] After adding two minor amendments to the recommendations of its ad hoc committee, the Advisory Committee adopted the bylaws. Though these bylaws effected no major changes in the operation of SMSG, certain aspects of them are worth noting. For one thing, the Advisory Committee elected to change its name to Advisory Board, and will be so referred to hereafter. For another, it made provision for rotating membership on the board, each member to have a three-year term; thus, one-third of the Board was to be replaced each year. This meant eight new members each year, and since the Conference on Future Responsibilities for School Mathematics had recommended that the Conference Board of the Mathematical Sciences have a hand in naming members, provision was made for the appointment, each year, of four members by the Conference Board. The other four members would be appointed by the SMSG Advisory Board itself. Consequently, each three years would witness a complete turnover in the membership of the Advisory Board for the group. The functions of the Advisory Board would remain essentially those of the former Advisory Committee.

Of more fundamental importance than the formalization of the SMSG organizational structure, however, was the formulation of a new statement of purpose for SMSG, a purpose substantially broader than that enunciated at the time SMSG was formed. As the new bylaws put it, "The primary purpose of the School Mathematics Study Group is to foster research and development in the teaching of school mathematics." Implicit in this statement, of course, was the notion that this "research and development" would improve the mathematics education offered by the schools of the United States. More-

3. See Appendix, List 31.

Reorganization

over, this research and development was to be a continuing concern of SMSG, one that would extend for an indefinite period of time.

When the bylaws were published in *Newsletter 11*, March 1962, three new panels were announced, on tests, on programed learning, and on small publications.[4] The first of these, the panel on tests, was a direct outgrowth of the work SMSG had conducted for the past two years in the field of psychology. The new panel would have, as a first major project, the supervision of a long-term study of the effectiveness of the new mathematics curricula. The project was an ambitious one, planned to extend over a period of five years or longer. It would involve a large number of students in many kinds of schools. Students at three different grade levels, 4th, 7th, and 10th, would be selected for study, and a large quantity of information on these students would be assembled. The scholastic progress of the students would be followed, year by year, sometimes by sample and sometimes by testing the entire group. Comparisons would be made using matched pairs of students, one enrolled in a traditional program and one in a course of the kind prepared by SMSG or similar groups. It was felt that a long-term study of this type was essential if objective data were to be obtained for purposes of evaluating the effectiveness of the new programs.

There were formidable problems involved in designing the experiment, not the least of which was finding schools that seemed likely to maintain a traditional type of offering throughout the period of the study. It was clearly impossible to bind any school to a particular type of program over a period of years, and all that could be done was to locate schools whose administrators felt it likely that no changes would be undertaken during the period. To factor out individual teacher differences, local school situations, dropouts, transfers, and other such variables, the number of students involved originally would have to be quite large, perhaps 100,000. By June

4. See Appendix, Lists 28, 32, and 33.

1962, however, a satisfactory number of schools had agreed to participate in the study, and the experiment was set to get under way in September.

The panel on programed learning was to supervise all SMSG matters pertaining to programed materials. The initial project involving such materials, which had been launched at Yale during the summer of 1961, progressed rapidly during the 1961–62 academic year. The twelve writing centers produced material at a good rate, and channeled it through SMSG headquarters to six reviewers, whose job it was to criticize the work and make suggestions for improvement. The material was then sent back to the writers for revision. When the revised programs were sent to headquarters, they were reproduced in quantity and sent to one of the twenty schools that were serving as testing centers for the initial stages of the project. The next summer's writing session would then revise the programs again in the light of the field-test data, and September would find 103 school districts and some 10,000 students using the revised programs as part of the experiment to test the relative effectiveness of the material.

The panel on small publications was to supervise the production of two kinds of publications. The first was to consist of supplementary material, especially material for the more able students. The second would consist of units that teachers could employ to introduce new ideas into their classes but that were not extensive enough to provide the basis of a completely new full-year course. The first of these small publications was due for production in the academic year 1962–63.

Another new SMSG project was to translate some of the SMSG materials into Spanish for use in testing Spanish-speaking Americans in the schools of Puerto Rico.[5] It was felt that the mathematics education of the Spanish-speaking citizen of the United States was a matter of concern to all Americans, and that a translation of SMSG textbooks into Spanish would go far to remove the barrier to understanding. The first books

5. See Appendix, List 34.

Reorganization

chosen for translation were those at the 7th and 9th grade levels, and it was anticipated that translations of the 8th and 10th grade books would follow. Two centers were involved in the project, one at the University of Puerto Rico and the other at Stanford. The texts would be available for use in September 1962.

SMSG had long given attention to the place of motion pictures and television in the field of mathematics education. Other pressing problems had seemed to demand priority, however, and little had been done in this regard until 1962. Then, in early June of that year, the Mathematical Association of America, the National Council of Teachers of Mathematics, and SMSG jointly sponsored a Conference on Mathematical Films. The conference was held in Chicago and included as participants forty prominent persons from all areas of the field of mathematics education.[6] The purpose of the conference was to explore the various ways in which motion pictures could be used to improve the teaching of mathematics, and to allot particular problems to each of the sponsoring organizations. This parceling out of spheres of interest was designed to prevent wasteful and time-consuming duplication of effort. The conference produced a number of resolutions, the chief one being that the presidents of the MAA and NCTM together with the Director of SMSG meet to establish an Interim Central Coordinating Committee.[7] This committee would be jointly supported by the three organizations and would have the responsibility of establishing a permanent Mathematics Film Center. This Mathematics Film Center would serve to coordinate all the work of the three groups in the area of mathematics films. In particular, it was recommended that SMSG be primarily concerned with films for the in-service training of teachers, and that it also concentrate on experimental work in films and the evaluation of mathematics films. By the end of June, SMSG was engaged in preliminary

6. See Appendix, List 35.
7. See Appendix, List 36.

SMSG: The Making of a Curriculum

writing for a film designed for elementary school teachers on modern aspects of the teaching of mathematics.

During the 1961–62 academic year, the panel on monographs presented to the public the first six of its monographs. These were:

1. *Numbers: Rational and Irrational* by Ivan Niven
2. *What Is Calculus About?* by W. W. Sawyer
3. *An Introduction to Inequalities* by Edwin Beckenbach and Richard Bellman
4. *Geometric Inequalities* by Nicholas D. Kazarinoff
5. *The Contest Problem Book: Problems from the Annual High School Contests of the Mathematical Association of America,* compiled by Charles T. Salkind
6. *The Lore of Large Numbers* by Philip J. Davis

They were published simultaneously by SMSG and Random House. SMSG, it will be recalled, had to assume publication of the school versions of these monographs on its own. It was a function, however, of which they were anxious to divest themselves, and in November 1961 arrangements were concluded with the L. W. Singer Company to take over this job. The next monograph in the series, *The Uses of Infinity* by Leo Zippin, was produced in the spring of 1962, this time by Random House and the L. W. Singer Company. Several more monographs were in various stages of production by the summer of that year.

The publication and distribution of material was always something of an undesired appendage of SMSG, and another step was taken in December 1961 to remove some more of this sort of activity from their immediate supervision. Arrangements were concluded with the A. C. Vroman Company, of Pasadena, California, by which this company would assume responsibility for the distribution of all SMSG publications except newsletters, monographs, and the completed textbooks handled by the Yale University Press. This, of course, resulted in a short period of renewed confusion with respect to the

Reorganization

ordering of SMSG materials. Wherever possible, however, orders directed to the wrong address were forwarded to the appropriate place for filling.

The Advisory Board held its usual three meetings during the period from September 1961 to June 1962. In addition to adopting the bylaws reorganizing SMSG, it considered a host of other matters. Each meeting of the Advisory Board always included a review of all phases of the work of SMSG. Each panel presented a brief survey of its own activities. The work of such ad hoc committees as were currently in existence was reviewed, and new matters of interest to SMSG were discussed. For example, one of the new subjects discussed during the year was that of gifted children. It was pointed out that, in many cases, local schools were unable to make provision for a really remarkable student. An ad hoc committee for the Advisory Board was appointed to investigate the problem and to make recommendations for actions that could be carried out by various mathematical organizations to help these schools.[8] Other matters considered by the Advisory Board were the beginning work on a 12th grade calculus text, the possible use of programed material for in-service training of elementary teachers, a request from the Turkish Society for Pure and Applied Mathematics for permission to translate SMSG materials, and the withdrawal of SMSG textbooks from the market.

The last question was a serious one, and an ad hoc committee was appointed to recommend procedures to be used in effecting such withdrawal.[9] SMSG was in a particularly delicate position regarding its textbooks. On the one hand, it had absolutely no desire to publish its books on a large scale or to enter in any way into competition with private enterprise in this area. On the other hand, its avowed purpose was to do what it could to improve the teaching of mathematics in the schools of the country, and, in the absence of commercial

8. See Appendix, List 37.
9. See Appendix, List 38.

textbooks of a comparable nature, it felt duty-bound to distribute its own revised materials to any school or district that wanted to use them. However, the years 1961 and 1962 saw several new commercial textbooks enter the marketplace, and the question of establishing withdrawal criteria became pressing. SMSG wanted at all costs to avoid the charge of attempting to establish a national curriculum. Still, it did not want to stop publishing its textbook for a particular grade level simply because a new commercial offering for that level had the word "modern" in its title.

What was needed was a set of well-defined criteria for such action at each grade level, criteria by which any given book could be objectively evaluated. The criteria could not be such that in any way channeled the outline of the book, but they had to be concrete enough to be clearly applicable. The items would, of course, have to be primarily concerned with content and presentation. Such matters as the wording of definitions, the structural properties of the subject, the avoidance of incorrect statements, and the inclusion of certain well-specified new material would clearly be relevant. As the academic year 1961–62 ended, this matter was being given the close attention of the Advisory Board, and early action was anticipated.

The spring semester of 1962 marked the beginning of the fifth year of SMSG's existence, and with it came the annual problem of the summer writing session. Manpower problems, supply problems, typing problems, and the like had become a part of the yearly cycle of SMSG, and while the experience of four years had served to make the problems familiar, and even, to some extent, easier of solution, it had not eliminated them. The fifth writing session was to be held at Stanford. The groups involved would be those concerned with the 8th grade, 7M and 9M, elementary school, geometry with coordinates, and programed learning. Some additional preparation would be made for the widespread testing necessary in September as part of the long-range study. As usual, the session convened on time, and, with its opening, the time span with which this history is concerned drew to a close.

8 Reactions to SMSG

It is too early to assess the full impact of the work of SMSG on the teaching of mathematics in the United States and elsewhere; the passage of many years will be necessary before a judgment of this kind can be made. The reception thus far accorded the efforts of SMSG by various interested groups has, however, been quite gratifying and gives some indication that its influence will be of a lasting and significant nature. Among these interested groups are students, teachers, teachers of teachers, parents, education administrators, and the mathematicians.

Students who have used SMSG materials appear to have reacted very favorably. Since it began testing its sample textbooks, SMSG has obtained thousands of detailed reports on the experiences of teachers using the experimental versions of the textbooks. Each of the reports covered one chapter of one book. Among items discussed by these teachers were some concerning the attitude and behavior of the students in the experimental classrooms. In overwhelming numbers, these teachers reported that students seemed more interested in studying mathematics than they formerly had been, and that classroom sessions were very simulating and challenging to teacher and student alike. Given a choice, a great majority of these students stated that they would prefer to continue studying mathematics from SMSG materials.

135

SMSG: The Making of a Curriculum

Though student attitudes toward SMSG materials are important from the standpoints of motivation and the effect of motivation on the learning of mathematics, of even greater importance is the impact of the subject matter itself on their future knowledge of mathematics. In the final analysis, the sole purpose of the Group has been to try to increase the sum total of such knowledge, both in the individual and in the society as a whole. The massive efforts made to improve textbooks, teaching, and other factors bearing on mathematics instruction have all been undertaken with a view toward their ultimate effect on this knowledge. The difference the study of SMSG materials will make on the students' future knowledge of mathematics cannot yet be determined, however, and is one question the future alone can answer.

Teachers who have used SMSG materials clearly consider them an improvement over what they had used in the past. Not only do the SMSG files reflect this attitude, but reports in the professional literature and at professional meetings by teachers using SMSG materials indicate the same thing. Most teachers who have taught from SMSG textbooks have had their viewpoints toward mathematics irrevocably changed, and will never return to teaching the same courses from a conventional point of view. This does not mean that every teacher using SMSG textual material approves of every aspect of its content, or agrees that everything therein is beyond improvement. Teachers have never felt this way toward any textbook or series of textbooks, and doubtless never will. But it is very clear that almost all the teachers who have used SMSG texts look upon them as presenting significantly better mathematics, in a much more meaningful manner, than those to which they have been accustomed.

Educators charged with the responsibility of training the teachers for our schools have a clear interest in the work of SMSG. As has been stated over and over again here and elsewhere, no lasting or significant improvement in mathematics education is possible without the approval and cooperation of

Reactions to SMSG

a corps of adequately trained teachers. While the in-service training of teachers is a formidable problem demanding massive effort on the part of many agencies, the responsibility for the mathematical training of those young people now in college who are preparing themselves for teaching careers devolves jointly upon the departments and schools of education and the departments of mathematics in our institutions of higher learning. Not only must time be made available in the teacher-training program for adequate mathematical preparation, but, of equal importance, the subject matter dealt with must be appropriate to the future needs of the students.

Requests for SMSG materials by teacher-training institutions offer testimony that these institutions are cognizant of the work of the Group, and that this work is having some influence on their offerings. Recently published textbooks for courses in mathematics for teachers, almost without exception, refer to the influence of SMSG on their contents. The same is true of newer books on curriculum and on methods of teaching mathematics. Though SMSG has deliberately avoided any direct attempt to influence pre-service teacher training (this falls, properly, in the province of the Committee on the Undergraduate Program of the MAA), it is nevertheless apparent that the work of the Group is of importance in this area.

Another group with a manifest interest in the efforts of SMSG consists of the parents of the school children in this country. Reactions from parents have been mixed but, on the whole, indicate approval. One of the most frequent complaints has been that parents have some difficulty when trying to help their children with homework. This is a particularly shattering experience when the children are still in elementary school. Some school districts, when embarking on a curriculum change involving the use of SMSG materials, have found it helpful to conduct classes especially for parents at the same time. These classes have served to allay the apprehensions of most of the parents attending. Indeed, in many cases, once the parents have become aware of the nature of the new material they have become active supporters of the program. Such classes are the exception rather than the rule, however, and the problem of alerting parents to the need for an improved mathematics curriculum remains a serious one. While a community of informed and interested parents can be a powerful and positive asset in any attempt to improve the mathematical offerings of a school or district, the subject of mathematics in general, and the nature of the changes being suggested in particular, make the creation of such a community difficult.

Because the changes are of a technical nature and go to the heart of the subject, a thorough understanding and appreciation of them requires an outlay of time and effort on the part of parents, an outlay that many of them are, quite understandably, unwilling to extend. In the absence of a thorough knowledge of mathematics, most parents find it necessary to accept the word of specialists that the changes being advocated for the mathematics curriculum are constructive. The SMSG newsletters might serve in a small way to alleviate some parental disquiet, but the mailing list is not that extensive. A great deal remains to be done to inform parents about needed changes in the school mathematics curriculum.

School administrators form another group interested in the activities of SMSG. In a very real sense, they are the most important group of all in any movement to reform the mathematics curriculum, for they are the ones who determine and administer it. SMSG encountered some rather paradoxical reactions from this group. A few administrators have charged SMSG with attempting to establish a national curriculum, despite the fact that the Group has leaned over backward to avoid giving any such impression. In the area of criticism of this kind, SMSG is clearly more sinned against than sinning. It has said over and over again that it does not consider its curriculum to be the only acceptable one. Professor Begle disavowed any such intent at the opening meeting of the original writing session at Yale in 1958, and clearly laid down the

Reactions to SMSG

reasons a national mathematics curriculum was both undesirable and unfeasible. SMSG's attitude with respect to this matter has never varied. It has never made any attempt to force its opinions or its products on any school district that does not desire them, nor will it ever do so. It has, however, never made any secret of the fact that it believes the mathematics curriculum (both for the college-capable students and for others) displayed in its sample textbooks is superior to traditional ones, and it has not stinted its efforts to bring its beliefs to the attention of mathematics educators at all levels. It has pointed out that there are other groups at work on the same problems and that the work of these groups is also worthy of the careful study of all those interested in mathematics education.

Fortunately, the number of administrators who believe SMSG is attempting to force their schools into some kind of a national mold is quite small. On the other side of the coin, SMSG has frequently had to face problems arising when administrators have tried to move too fast in incorporating SMSG materials into their programs and who have not first made sure that their teachers were prepared to handle them. As was explained in earlier chapters, when the sample textbooks were being class-tested, SMSG invariably provided the teachers participating in the tests with assistance in the form of mathematics consultants and commentaries for teachers. Every consideration was given to the fact that most teachers are not prepared to plunge instantly into a completely new program, particularly a program calling for a wholly new point of view toward mathematics. As a result, the class testing not only supplied SMSG with valuable data for revising and improving the textbooks, but also left participating school districts with a nucleus of enthusiastic and experienced teachers, each of whom could use modern mathematics materials in a highly effective way. This nucleus could, in turn, assist colleagues in any future transition to a modern curriculum, and, as a result, the districts participating in the class testing would be able to make such a transition with less difficulty than others.

When the revised sample textbooks were released for public sale, however, many schools and school districts that had not participated in the class-testing program rushed to purchase them without first making sure that their teachers were prepared to handle them, and without any thought to the provision of expert help for their teachers. Though such precipitate action sometimes sprang from a bandwagon attitude, it was more often the result of a sincerely held conviction that an improved mathematics curriculum was long overdue, and that the children in our schools were entitled to the best mathematics training the schools could provide.

Whatever the motivation, it was (and is) manifestly unwise to attempt to install a new kind of mathematics in a school where the teaching staff is not prepared to teach it. As a result of moving too fast, some schools attempting a wholesale transition to SMSG materials found themselves with a frustrated faculty, a confused student body, and a sadly disappointed administration. It is easy to understand how such an experience could lead the administration to cast a jaundiced eye upon the material itself. A negative attitude toward modern mathematics by administrators who have found themselves in this kind of difficulty is doubly unfortunate. Not only does SMSG acquire an undeservedly poor reputation in their eyes, but it is likely that their students will be deprived of any further attempt to improve their mathematics curriculum for some time to come.

SMSG has tried to prevent such unhappy occurrences by vigorously advocating that any transition from a traditional to a modern curriculum be carefully planned before being implemented, and that the mathematics teachers involved take an integral part in the planning. Although some districts have found that they could successfully install SMSG materials in their schools almost overnight, many others have found that

Reactions to SMSG

they were not in a position to do so until some attention had been given to the in-service training of their teachers. To ignore this need is to invite trouble and disappointment.

The reports made to SMSG by administrators who have adopted SMSG materials with due attention to their teaching staffs are quite favorable. Moreover, the sales records of SMSG textbooks bear testimony to the fact that, on the whole, schools and school districts that early elected to install the SMSG curriculum retained it. As time passes and more and more commercial textbooks qualitatively comparable to those of SMSG appear on the market, there seems little likelihood that these schools will ever return to a traditional curriculum.

Another group interested in the work of SMSG is the mathematicians. They were, after all, responsible for its formation. It has been said that mathematicians resemble French politicians in the passion with which they hold convictions as to how mathematics ought to be taught. The relatively small number of objections by them to what SMSG has done is, therefore, a tribute either to the well-publicized statement that SMSG is preparing only a sample program or to the general acceptability, by the mathematicians, of the results.

The only serious objection to SMSG textbooks agreed upon by more than a handful of mathematicians is concerned with applications of mathematics. It has been said that the material in SMSG sample textbooks does not lean heavily enough on the physical sciences for explication and motivation, and that the books do not contain enough examples of applications to scientific matters. It is true that applications of mathematics are not the chief concern of SMSG textual material. The reason for this is quite simple: there are many different applications for almost every mathematical concept. To the writers of the textbooks, it seemed of overriding importance that the concept involved be clear if the student was to be able to apply it in any one of a variety of situations. The examples used throughout the textbooks, therefore, came from a number of

141

different fields. Problems dealing with areas of physics, chemistry, biology, business, and the concerns of the consumer are all in evidence.

There are some who believe, however, that if mathematics is not continuously tied to physical models, it will not be understood and will not be appealing to the student. This is a point of view that was represented by some of the SMSG writers. The fact that it is not a point of view widely shared by mathematicians and high school teachers and supervisors is evidenced by the fact that not all the mathematics included in the SMSG textbooks is explicitly motivated by, or developed around, physical situations. It was the feeling of most of the writers of the SMSG textbooks that, contrary to the belief of some, not every teenager is fascinated by the behavior of freely falling bodies or enthralled with phenomena exhibited by gasses in closed or leaking containers. When, in the opinion of the school teachers and supervisors involved, physical motivation seemed desirable, it was included; when they felt it would serve no useful educational purpose, it was not. Nevertheless, to persons who are dedicated to the thesis that ideas as such are of little interest or concern to anyone, it may seem that SMSG did less than justice to their particular school of thought.

It is difficult to assess the extent to which criticisms of the foregoing nature are valid. As emphasized earlier, SMSG tried to encompass a wide variety of mathematical viewpoints and philosophies among its writers, and a careful examination of the list of participants will show that it was successful. What it has produced in the way of new textual material represents nothing more or less than a consensus of these diverse beliefs. If there indeed exists only one true mathematical philosophy, and if this philosophy is the one engendering the foregoing criticism, then to the extent the Group has compromised this philosophy it has erred. Pending revelation in this area, however, it sought long and hard for those topics and those approaches that most mathematicians and teachers in this coun-

Reactions to SMSG

try believe to be in the best interests of our youth, and it is these that constitute its sample curriculum.

It seems safe to say that, on balance, the reception given the work of SMSG by each of the groups enumerated earlier in this chapter has been favorable. Because these groups are those most directly concerned with the Group's efforts, there is little doubt that the influence SMSG has attempted to exert on the teaching of mathematics will be of lasting value. In a larger view, every American citizen has something at stake in the matter of the mathematical training of our youth. We find ourselves, willy-nilly, in the midst of a civilization whose dependency on mathematics is visibly increasing. We are beset on every side by problems of a magnitude inconceivable a few years ago, many of which are purely quantitative in nature, and some of which bear on the matter of our national survival. It is imperative that these problems be understood by every American and that the implications of any quantitative aspects they entail be appreciated. Our economists are becoming accustomed to rounding figures to tenths of a billion, while our scientists are deeply concerned with ways of increasing their accuracy in working with micro-micro-seconds. On the one hand, every citizen ought to know that the difference between 3.4 and 3.5 billion dollars is one hundred million dollars, and, on the other, it seems important to be aware of the fact that the dialogue involving micro-micro-seconds includes matters relevant to how long it will take to exterminate a million human beings.

In its collective wisdom, the Congress of the United States has dealt with some of the awesome problems facing the nation today by establishing the National Science Foundation and supporting it with a portion of the national income. Those in the Foundation charged with the responsibility of seeing that the funds appropriated for its use are wisely expended have foreseen that the solutions of many of these problems involve not only highly trained mathematical specialists, but a body politic each member of which is as well versed in mathematics as possible. Without the financial and moral support of the Congress and the Foundation, the work accomplished by the School Mathematics Study Group would not have been possible. Given this support, however, together with the talent of some of our most distinguished mathematicians, the wisdom and experience of a group of the nation's finest mathematics teachers and supervisors, and the indispensable leadership and guidance of Professor Begle, there is reason to hope that the work of SMSG will have an indirect but discernible and beneficial influence on the future welfare of the entire nation.

The work of the School Mathematics Study Group is not finished. What is detailed herein is but a brief outline of the first four years of its existence. With the adoption of a set of bylaws, the Group embarked on a new and, hopefully, permanent course. The early years have shown that classroom teachers and ivory-towered mathematicians can work together amicably and productively. Having established this rapport, SMSG will continue to seek ways and means of improving the mathematical education of our youth.

Appendix

All affiliations shown are those existing at time of appointment.

1. COMMISSION ON MATHEMATICS

    Carl B. Allendoerfer, University of Washington
    Edwin C. Douglas, The Taft School, Watertown, Connecticut
    Howard F. Fehr, Columbia University
    Martha Hildebrandt, Proviso Township High School,
      Maywood, Illinois
    Albert E. Meder, Jr., Rutgers University
    Morris Meister, Bronx High School of Science, New York City
    Frederick Mosteller, Harvard University
    Eugene P. Northrup, University of Chicago
    Ernest R. Ranucci, Weequahic High School, Newark,
      New Jersey
    Robert E. K. Rourke, Kent School, Kent, Connecticut
    George B. Thomas, Massachusetts Institute of Technology
    Albert W. Tucker, Princeton University
    Henry Van Engen, Iowa State Teachers College
    Samuel S. Wilks, Princeton University

2. PARTICIPANTS AT CONFERENCE ON TRAINING AND RESEARCH
POTENTIAL IN MATHEMATICS

    A. A. Albert, University of Chicago
    H. F. Bohnenblust, California Institute of Technology
    W. L. Chow, Johns Hopkins University

SMSG: The Making of a Curriculum

Leon Cohen, National Science Foundation
Richard Courant, New York University
Bowen Dees, National Science Foundation
J. L. Doob, University of Illinois
Samuel Eilenberg, Columbia University
John Gergen, Duke University
G. A. Hedlund, Yale University
M. R. Hestenes, University of California at Los Angeles
Edwin Hewitt, University of Washington
Harry C. Kelly, National Science Foundation
S. C. Kleene, University of Wisconsin
L. H. Loomis, Harvard University
S. MacLane, University of Chicago
E. J. McShane, University of Virginia
W. T. Martin, Massachusetts Institute of Technology
C. B. Morrey, Jr., University of California
B. J. Pettis, University of North Carolina
T. Rado, Ohio State University
P. C. Rosenbloom, University of Minnesota
H. Royden, Stanford University
Norman Steenrod, Princeton University
M. H. Stone, University of Chicago
F. E. Ulrich, Rice Institute
H. S. Wall, University of Texas
A. D. Wallace, Tulane University
Hassler Whitney, Institute for Advanced Study, Princeton University
R. L. Wilder, University of Michigan
J. W. T. Youngs, Indiana University
Daniel Zelinsky, Northwestern University

3. PARTICIPANTS AT THE CAMBRIDGE CONFERENCE
February 28–March 1, 1958

A. A. Albert, University of Chicago
D. B. Anderson, State College of North Carolina
R. V. Bartz, Massachusetts Institute of Technology
E. G. Begle, Yale University
Lipman Bers, New York University
R. H. Bing, University of Wisconsin

Appendix

    Frederick Bohnenblust, California Institute of Technology
    Richard Brauer, Harvard University
    S. S. Cairns, University of Illinois
    William Duren, University of Virginia
    F. L. Friedman, Massachusetts Institute of Technology
    A. M. Gleason, Harvard University
    A. G. Hedlund, Yale University
    P. W. Hemily, National Science Foundation
    H. C. Kelly, National Science Foundation
    E. J. McShane, University of Virginia
    W. T. Martin, Massachusetts Institute of Technology
    E. E. Moise, University of Michigan
    G. B. Price, University of Kansas
    Mina Rees, Hunter College
    P. C. Rosenbloom, University of Minnesota
    G. B. Thomas, Jr., Massachusetts Institute of Technology
    A. W. Tucker, Princeton University
    R. J. Walker, Cornell University
    J. L. Walsh, Harvard University
    R. L. Wilder, University of Michigan
    S. S. Wilks, Princeton University
    J. R. Zacharias, Massachusetts Institute of Technology

4. COMMITTEE APPOINTED TO ACT FOR CAMBRIDGE CONFERENCE

    A. A. Albert, University of Chicago
    R. L. Wilder, University of Michigan
    S. S. Wilks, Princeton University

5. PRESIDENTS, 1957–58

    MAA—G. Baley Price, University of Kansas
    NCTM—Harold P. Fawcett, Ohio State University

6. COMMITTEE OF EIGHT

    A. A. Albert, University of Chicago
    E. G. Begle, Yale University
    Lipman Bers, New York University
    A. E. Meder, Rutgers University
    G. B. Price, University of Kansas

SMSG: The Making of a Curriculum

Henry Van Engen, University of Wisconsin
R. L. Wilder, University of Michigan
S. S. Wilks, Princeton University

7. ORIGINAL ADVISORY COMMITTEE

A. A. Albert, University of Chicago
F. B. Allen, Lyons Township High School, LaGrange, Illinois
E. G. Begle, Yale University
Lipman Bers, New York University
S. S. Cairns, University of Illinois
G. F. Carrier, Harvard University
W. L. Duren, Jr., University of Virginia
Howard Fehr, Columbia University
H. V. Funk, Columbia University
A. M. Gleason, Harvard University
J. H. Hlavaty, Dewitt Clinton High School, New York City
P. S. Jones, University of Michigan
L. Clark Lay, Pasadena City College
K. O. May, Carleton College
J. R. Mayor, American Association for the Advancement of Science
A. E. Meder, Jr., Rutgers University
E. E. Moise, University of Michigan
P. M. Naghdi, University of California
Richard Pieters, Phillips Academy, Andover, Massachusetts
G. B. Price, University of Kansas
R. E. K. Rourke, Kent School, Kent, Connecticut
A. W. Tucker, Princeton University
Henry Van Engen, University of Wisconsin
A. D. Wallace, Tulane University
E. L. Walters, William Penn Senior High School, York, Pennsylvania
Marie S. Wilcox, Thomas Carr Howe High School, Indianapolis, Indiana
M. W. Zemansky, The College of the City of New York, New York

Appendix

8. ORIGINAL EXECUTIVE COMMITTEE OF FIVE

    A. A. Albert, University of Chicago
    A. M. Gleason, Harvard University
    J. H. Hlavaty, De Witt Clinton High School, New York City
    A. E. Meder, Rutgers University
    R. S. Pieters, Phillips Academy, Andover, Massachusetts

9. PARTICIPANTS IN WRITING SESSION AT YALE UNIVERSITY, 1958

    F. B. Allen, Lyons Township High School, LaGrange, Illinois
    E. F. Beckenbach, The RAND Corporation
    R. H. Bing, University of Wisconsin
    J. A. Brown, State University Teachers College, Oneonta, N.Y.
    Hope Chipman, University High School, Ann Arbor, Michigan
    Mary P. Dolciani, Hunter College
    E. C. Douglas, The Taft School, Watertown, Connecticut
    E. A. Dudley, North Haven High School, North Haven, Connecticut
    Florence Elder, Hempstead High School, West Hempstead, N.Y.
    W. E. Ferguson, Newton High School, Newtonville, Massachusetts
    Joyce D. Fontaine, North Haven High School, North Haven, Connecticut
    E. Glenadine Gibb, Iowa State Teachers College
    R. A. Good, University of Maryland
    Lenore John, University High School, University of Chicago
    B. W. Jones, University of Colorado
    M. L. Keedy, University of Maryland
    Marguerite Lehr, Bryn Mawr College
    Eunice Lewis, Laboratory High School, University of Oklahoma
    M. Albert Linton, Jr., William Penn Charter School, Philadelphia, Pa.
    J. R. Mayor, American Association for the Advancement of Science
    K. G. Michaels, North Haven High School, North Haven, Connecticut
    E. E. Moise, University of Michigan
    E. P. Northrop, University of Chicago
    O. J. Peterson, Kansas State Teachers College, Emporia, Kansas

R. S. Pieters, Phillips Academy, Andover, Massachusetts
H. O. Pollak, Bell Telephone Laboratories, Murray Hill, New Jersey
G. B. Price, University of Kansas
Persis Redgrave, Norwich Free Academy, Norwich, Connecticut
D. E. Richmond, Dartmouth College
C. E. Rickart, Yale University
P. C. Rosenbloom, University of Minnesota
M. F. Rosskopf, Teachers College, Columbia University
Harry Ruderman, Bronx High School of Science, Bronx, N.Y.
Veryl Schult, District of Columbia Public Schools
Henry Swain, New Trier Township High School, Winnetka, Illinois
A. W. Tucker, Princeton University
H. E. Vaughan, University of Illinois
John Wagner, University of Texas
R. J. Walker, Cornell University
A. D. Wallace, Tulane University
William Wooton, Verdugo Hills High School, Tujunga, California

10. 7TH AND 8TH GRADE CENTERS (chairman's name followed by consultant's)

   University of Arizona: F. L. Bedford, A. H. Steinbrenner
   Brookline, Massachusetts: R. F. Ward, G. B. Thomas
   University of Chicago: Lenore John, Margaret S. Matchett
   University of Colorado: W. E. Briggs, W. M. Richardson
   University of Delaware: J. A. Brown, W. E. Baxter
   Louisiana State University: H. T. Karnes (chairman and consultant)
   University of Michigan: P. S. Jones (chairman and consultant)
   University of Minnesota: P. C. Rosenbloom, Donovan A. Johnson
   Pasadena, California: W. G. Norris, R. A. Dean
   Princeton, New Jersey: Ruth Law, L. R. Welch
   Seattle, Washington: N. L. Massey, R. A. Beaumont
   Westport, Connecticut: Ray Walch, E. G. Begle

Appendix

11. SPEAKERS AT CONFERENCE ON CENTERS FOR GRADES 7 AND 8, November 21 and 22, 1958, Washington, D.C.

E. G. Begle, Director, School Mathematics Study Group
J. A. Brown, University of Delaware
Mrs. Helen Cooper, North Bethesda Junior High School, Bethesda, Maryland
W. J. Fleming, Montgomery County Schools, Rickville, Maryland
Mrs. Tempie Franklin, Arlington County Board of Education, Arlington, Virginia
Mrs. Helen Garstens, Associate Director, UMMaP
Mrs. Ethel Grubbs, Washington, D.C. Public Schools
J. W. Gustad, University of Maryland
T. P. Hillman, Gunston Junior High School, Arlington, Virginia
Lenore John, University of Chicago
Patricia Johnson, Belt Junior High School, Wheaton, Maryland
B. W. Jones, University of Colorado
P. S. Jones, University of Michigan
M. L. Keedy, University of Maryland
T. S. Klein, Prince Georges County Public Schools, Upper Marlboro, Maryland
Roberta R. Lynch, Benjamin Stoddert Junior High School, Washington, D.C.
G. T. Preston, Browne Junior High School, Washington, D.C.
P. C. Rosenbloom, University of Minnesota
Veryl Schult, Washington, D.C., Public Schools

12. PANEL ON 7TH AND 8TH GRADES

J. A. Brown, State University Teachers College, Oneonta, New York
Lenore John, University of Chicago
B. W. Jones, University of Colorado
P. S. Jones, University of Michigan
J. R. Mayor, American Association for the Advancement of Science
P. C. Rosenbloom, University of Minnesota
Veryl Schult, Supervisor of Mathematics, Washington, D.C.

SMSG: The Making of a Curriculum

13. PANEL ON SAMPLE TEXTBOOKS

F. B. Allen, Lyons Township High School, LaGrange, Illinois
Edwin Douglas, The Taft School, Watertown, Connecticut
D. E. Richmond, Williams College, Williamstown, Massachusetts
C. E. Rickart, Yale University
Henry Swain, New Trier Township High School, Winnetka, Illinois
R. J. Walker, Cornell University

14. PANEL ON MONOGRAPHS (ORIGINAL)

Lipman Bers, New York University, New York
H. S. M. Coxeter, University of Toronto, Toronto, Ontario, Canada
P. R. Halmos, University of Chicago
J. H. Hlavaty, Dewitt Clinton High School, New York
N. Jacobsen, Yale University
H. O. Pollak, Bell Telephone Laboratories
George Polya, Stanford University
R. S. Pieters, Phillips Academy, Andover, Massachusetts
H. E. Robbins, Columbia University
W. W. Sawyer, Wesleyan University
N. E. Steenrod, Princeton University
J. J. Stoker, New York University
Leo Zippin, Queens College, Flushing, New York

15. PANEL ON TEACHER TRAINING

J. B. Adkins, Phillips Exeter Academy, Exeter, New Hampshire
H. F. Fehr, Columbia University
J. L. Kelley, University of California
L. C. Lay, Pasadena City College
K. O. May, Carleton College
B. E. Meserve, Montclair State Teachers College, Montclair, New Jersey
G. S. Young, University of Michigan

Appendix

16. SPEAKERS AT CONFERENCE ON ELEMENTARY SCHOOL MATHEMATICS, Chicago, February 13 and 14, 1959

    William A. Brownell, University of California (Berkeley)
    Howard F. Fehr, Columbia University
    E. Glenadine Gibb, Iowa State Teachers College
    John W. Gustad, University of Maryland
    Newton S. Hawley, Stanford University
    David A. Page, University of Illinois
    Anita P. Riess, University of Bridgeport
    Paul C. Rosenbloom, University of Minnesota
    Catherine Stern, New York City
    Marshall H. Stone, University of Chicago
    Patrick C. Suppes, Stanford University
    Donald W. Taylor, Yale University

17. 1959 WRITING TEAMS COMBINED

    H. W. Alexander, Earlham College
    Frank B. Allen, Lyons Township High School, LaGrange, Illinois
    R. D. Anderson, Louisiana State University
    B. H. Arnold, Oregon State College
    Alexander Beck, Olney High School, Philadelphia, Pa.
    E. F. Beckenbach, University of California at Los Angeles
    Paul Berg, Stanford University
    Emil Berger, Monroe High School, St. Paul, Minnesota
    Arthur Bernhart, University of Oklahoma
    R. H. Bing, University of Wisconsin
    A. A. Blank, New York University
    Shirley Boselly, Franklin High School, Seattle, Washington
    John A. Brown, University of Delaware
    Kenneth E. Brown, Department of Health, Education and Welfare
    J. M. Calloway, Carleton College
    Hope Chipman, University High School, Ann Arbor, Michigan
    R. R. Christian, University of British Columbia
    R. J. Clark, St. Paul's School, Concord, N.H.
    Mildred B. Cole, East Aurora Jr. High Sch., Aurora, Illinois
    B. H. Colvin, Boeing Scientific Research Laboratories
    J. A. Cooley, University of Tennessee

SMSG: The Making of a Curriculum

P. H. Daus, University of California at Los Angeles
R. B. Davis, Syracuse University
R. A. Dean, California Institute of Technology
Charles DePrima, California Institute of Technology
Mary P. Dolciani, Hunter College
E. C. Douglas, The Taft School, Watertown, Connecticut
Floyds Downs, East High School, Denver, Colorado
E. A. Dudley, North Haven High School, North Haven, Connecticut
Lincoln Durst, The Rice Institute
Florence Elder, West Hempstead Jr.-Sr. High School, West Hempstead, N.Y.
Marion G. Epstein, Educational Testing Service, Princeton, N.Y.
W. E. Ferguson, Newton High School, Newtonville, Massachusetts
N. J. Fine, University of Pennsylvania
Joyce D. Fontaine, North Haven High School, North Haven, Connecticut
Helen Garstens, University of Maryland
Esther O. Gassett, Claremore High School, Claremore, Oklahoma
H. M. Gehman, University of Buffalo
L. Roland Genise, North Junior High School, Brentwood, N.Y.
R. K. Getoor, University of Washington
E. Glenadine Gibb, State College of Iowa
R. A. Good, University of Maryland
V. H. Haag, Franklin and Marshall College
Alice Hach, Racine Public Schools, Racine, Wisconsin
R. R. Hartman, Edine-Morningside Senior High School, Minneapolis, Minnesota
M. H. Heins, University of Illinois
Edwin Hewitt, University of Washington
Martha Hildebrandt, Proviso Township High School, Maywood, Illinois
S. B. Jackson, University of Maryland
Lenore John, Laboratory School, University of Chicago
B. W. Jones, University of Colorado
P. S. Jones, University of Michigan
R. C. Jurgensen, Culver Miltary Academy, Culver, Indiana
H. T. Karnes, Louisiana State University

Appendix

M. L. Keedy, University of Maryland
Mildred Keiffer, Cincinnati Public Schools, Cincinnati, Ohio
Joseph Lehner, Michigan State University
Kenneth Leisenring, University of Michigan
Eunice Lewis, Laboratory High School, University of Oklahoma
M. A. Linton, William Penn Charter School, Philadelphia, Pa.
A. E. Livingston, University of Washington
L. H. Loomis, Harvard University
Nick Lovdjieff, Anthony Junior High School, Minneapolis, Minnesota
R. V. Lynch, Phillips Exeter Academy, Exeter, N.H.
Helen Marston, Douglass College
J. R. Mayor, American Association for the Advancement of Science
W. K. McNabb, Hockaday School, Dallas, Texas
S. S. Meyers, Educational Testing Service, Princeton, N.J.
K. G. Michaels, North Haven High School, North Haven, Connecticut
Muriel Mills, Hill Junior High School, Denver, Colorado
E. E. Moise, University of Michigan
O. J. Peterson, Kansas State Teachers College
B. J. Pettis, University of North Carolina
R. S. Pieters, Phillips Academy, Andover, Massachusetts
Charles F. Pinzka, University of Cincinnati
H. O. Pollak, Bell Telephone Laboratories
Walter Prenowitz, Brooklyn College
G. Baley Price, University of Kansas
A. L. Putnam, University of Chicago
Persis O. Redgrave, Norwich Free Academy, Norwich, Connecticut
Mina Rees, Hunter College
D. E. Richmond, Williams College
C. E. Rickart, Yale University
P. C. Rosenbloom, University of Minnesota
Elizabeth Roudebush, Seattle Public Schools, Seattle, Washington
Harry Ruderman, Hunter College High School, New York City
George Schaefer, Alexis I. Dupont High School, Wilmington, Delaware

Veryl Schult, Washington, D.C. Public Schools
J. T. Schwartz, New York University
O. E. Stanaitis, St. Olaf College, Northfield, Minnesota
Robert Starkey, Cubberley High School, Palo Alto, California
Philip P. Stucky, Roosevelt High School, Seattle, Washington
Henry Swain, New Trier Township High School, Winnetka, Illinois
Henry W. Syer, The Kent School, Kent, Connecticut
G. B. Thomas, Jr., Massachusetts Institute of Technology
A. W. Tucker, Princeton University
John Wagner, University of Texas
Ray Walch, Westport Public Schools, Westport, Connecticut
R. J. Walker, Cornell University
A. D. Wallace, Tulane, University
E. L. Walters, William Penn Sr. High School, York, Pa.
F. C. Watson, East High School, Rochester, N.Y.
Warren B. White, North High School, Sheboygan, Wisconsin
D. V. Widder, Harvard University
A. B. Willcox, Amherst College
William Wooton, Pierce Junior College, Woodland Hills, California

18. 1959–60 CENTERS (chairman's name followed by consultant's)

Grade 9

San Francisco Bay Area: Justin M. Bardellini, David W. Blakeslee
Boston: Martha Zelinka, Elmer B. Mode
Cincinnati: Mildred Keiffer, G. M. Merriman
Enid, Oklahoma: Lysle C. Mason, chairman-consultant
Muskogee, Oklahoma: Claude Harris, Herbert V. Monks
New Trier Township, Illinois: Henry Swain, A. L. Putnam
North Carolina: B. J. Pettis, chairman-consultant
San Francisco Peninsula: George Truscott, George E. Forsythe
Proviso, Illinois: Martha Hildebrandt, chairman-consultant
Santa Clara, California: Roger S. Bagnall, John L. Marks
Seattle: Arthur Livingston, chairman-consultant

Grade 10

San Francisco Bay Area: Jesse K. Peckenham, Henry Helson

Appendix

    Boston: Robert Bateman, Donald L. Dreider
    Charlottesville: William Lowry, E. J. McShane
    Colorado: Leon Rutland, chairman-consultant
    Durant, Oklahoma: L. A. Dwight, chairman-consultant
    Oklahoma City: Thomas H. Hill, Eunice Lewis
    North Carolina: R. R. Bernard, chairman-consultant
    San Francisco Peninsula: Alexandra Forsythe, Harold Bacon
    Santa Clara: Frank Burrows, Max Kramer
    Seattle: Albert Nyenhuis
    Suburban Philadelphia: M. Albert Linton, Cletus O. Oakley

    Grade 11

    San Francisco Bay: Lawrence Hawkinson & Hargrave Swift (co-chairmen), Bernard Friedman
    Boston: M. Philbrick Bridgess, Francis Scheid
    Edmond: Dorothea Meagher, chairman-consultant
    North Carolina: E. A. Cameron, chairman-consultant
    Peninsula: Robert Starkey, Paul Berg
    Santa Clara: James Buttcane, James R. Smart
    St. Paul: Emil Berger, Walter Fleming
    Tulsa: C. C. Pruitt, R. W. Beatch
    Weatherford: Gerald Goff, chairman-consultant

    Grade 12

    Boston: John Moulton, Louis N. Howard
    Dallas: D. E. Edmondson, chairman-consultant
    Houston: Ella Porter, L. K. Durst
    Peninsula: Sarah Herriot, John G. Herriot
    Philadelphia: Karl S. Kalman, Walter Lawton
    Santa Clara: Claire E. Christensen, Howard W. Myers

19. SPEAKERS AT ORIENTATION CONFERENCE FOR SMSG EXPERIMENT CENTERS, Chicago, September 19, 1959

    E. G. Begle (Introduction)
    Frank B. Allen, Lyons Township High School, LaGrange, Illinois
    E. F. Beckenbach, University of California at Los Angeles
    Paul Berg, Stanford University
    Hope Chipman, University High School, Ann Arbor, Michigan
    Mildred Cole, East Aurora Junior High School, Aurora, Illinois

P. H. Daus, University of California at Los Angeles
Robert Davis, Syracuse University
Edwin Dudley, North Haven High School, North Haven, Connecticut
L. K. Durst, The Rice Institute
Florence Elder, West Hempstead High School, West Hempstead, New York
W. E. Ferguson, Newton High School, Newtonville, Massachusetts
Esther O. Gassett, Claremore High School, Claremore, Oklahoma
V. H. Haag, Franklin and Marshall College
Martha Hildebrandt, Proviso Township High School, Maywood, Illinois
S. B. Jackson, University of Maryland
Ray Jurgensen, Culver Miltary Academy, Culver, Indiana
M. Albert Linton, William Penn Charter School, Philadelphia, Pennsylvania
Nick Lovdjieff, Anthony Junior High School, Minneapolis, Minnesota
J. R. Mayor, American Association for the Advancement of Science
W. K. McNabb, Hockaday School, Dallas, Texas
E. E. Moise, University of Michigan
H. O. Pollak, Bell Telephone Laboratories
Walter Prenowitz, Brooklyn College
G. Baley Price, University of Kansas
D. E. Richmond, Williams College
C. E. Rickart, Yale University
P. C. Rosenbloom, University of Minnesota
Harry Ruderman, Hunter College High School, New York City
Veryl Schult, Washington, D.C., Public Schools
Henry Swain, New Trier Township High School, Winnetka, Illinois
A. B. Willcox, Amherst College

20. PANEL ON ELEMENTARY SCHOOL MATHEMATICS

Leslie Beatty, Chula Vista City School District, Chula Vista, California

Appendix

    E. Glenadine Gibb, Iowa State Teachers College
    W. T. Guy, University of Texas
    S. B. Jackson, University of Maryland
    Irene Sauble, Detroit Public Schools
    M. H. Stone, University of Chicago
    J. F. Weaver, Boston University
    R. L. Wilder, University of Michigan

21. ELEMENTARY MATHEMATICS PLANNING SESSION, May 5–12, 1960

    Mildred Cole, East Aurora Junior High School, Aurora, Illinois
    J. A. Cooley, University of Tennessee
    E. Glenadine Gibb, Iowa State Teachers College
    W. T. Guy, University of Texas
    Stanley B. Jackson, University of Maryland
    Lenore John, University High School, University of Chicago
    J. R. Mayor, American Association for the Advancement of Science
    Irene Sauble, Detroit Public Schools
    Helen A. Schneider, Oak School, LaGrange, Illinois
    Marshall H. Stone, University of Chicago
    J. Fred Weaver, Boston University

22. PANEL ON NON-COLLEGE-BOUND STUDENTS

    V. H. Haag, Franklin and Marshall College
    Mildred Keiffer, Cincinatti Board of Education
    Oscar Schaaf, South Eugene High School, Eugene, Oregon
    M. A. Sobel, Montclair State College, Upper Montclair, New Jersey
    Marie Wilcox, Thomas Carr Howe High School, Indianapolis, Indiana
    A. B. Willcox, Amherst College

23. COMMITTEE ON APPLICATIONS OF PSYCHOLOGY, Stanford, July 19, 1960

    Richard Alpert, Harvard University
    L. W. Doob, Yale University
    Edward Swanson, University of Minnesota

SMSG: The Making of a Curriculum

24. PARTICIPANTS IN SUMMER WRITING SESSION, 1960

Frank B. Allen, Lyons Township High School, LaGrange, Illinois
Richard Alpert, Harvard University
R. D. Anderson, Louisiana State University
E. F. Beckenbach, University of California at Los Angeles
Paul W. Berg, Stanford University
Emil J. Berger, Monroe High School, St. Paul, Minnesota
R. H. Bing, University of Wisconsin
T. A. Botts, University of Virginia
K. E. Brown, U.S. Office of Education
J. M. Calloway, Kalamazoo College, Kalamazoo, Michigan
Hope H. Chipman, University High School, Ann Arbor, Michigan
Ronald J. Clark, St. Paul's School, Concord, New Hampshire
Mildred B. Cole, K. D. Waldo Junior High School, Aurora, Illinois
B. H. Colvin, Boeing Scientific Research Labs.
J. A. Cooley, University of Tennessee
Helen L. Curran, Glenview School, Oakland, California
C. R. DePrima, California Institute of Technology
F. L. Downs, Kent School, Kent, Connecticut
E. A. Dudley, North Haven High School, North Haven, Connecticut
L. K. Durst, William Rice University
Marion G. Epstein, Educational Testing Service
Florence Elder, West Hempstead High School, West Hempstead, N.Y.
Walter Fleming, Hamline University
Helen L. Garstens, University of Maryland
Esther Gassett, Kent School, Kent, Connecticut
H. M. Gehman, University of Buffalo
L. R. Genise, Brentwood Public Schools, Brentwood, N.Y.
E. Glenadine Gibb, Iowa State Teachers College
W. T. Guy, Jr., University of Texas
V. H. Haag, Franklin and Marshall College, Lancaster, Pa.
Leon Haaland, Kenwood School, Minneapolis, Minnesota
Clarence Ethel Hardgrove, Northern Illinois University

Appendix

R. S. Hargrove, Corpus Christi Public Schools, Corpus Christi, Texas
R. R. Hartman, Edina-Morningside High School, Minneapolis, Minnesota
Sarah T. Herriot, Cubberley Senior High School, Palo Alto, California
A. A. Hiatt, Santa Clara High School, Santa Clara, California
T. J. Hill, Oklahoma City Public Schools, Oklahoma City, Oklahoma
Max Hosier, Iowa State Teachers College
Lucille Houston, McKinley Junior High School, Racine, Wisconsin
Helen L. Hughes, Theodore Roosevelt Jr. High School, Eugene, Oregon
H. G. Jacob, Louisiana State University
Lenore John, University High School, University of Chicago
Donovan Johnson, University of Minnesota
B. W. Jones, University of Colorado
P. S. Jorgensen, Carleton College, Northfield, Minnesota
Ray Jurgensen, Culver Miltary Academy, Culver, Indiana
H. T. Karnes, Louisiana State University
Mildred Keiffer, Cincinnati Public Schools, Cincinnati, Ohio
D. H. Knowles, Samuel Ayer High School, Milpitas, California
C. J. Koutsopoulos, Educational Testing Service
Howard Levi, Columbia University
Emma M. Lewis, Washington D.C. Public Schools
Eunice Lewis, University School, University of Oklahoma
M. A. Linton, Jr., William Penn Charter School, Philadelphia, Pa.
W. G. Lister, State University of New York
Nick Lovdjieff, Anthony Junior High School, Minneapolis, Minnesota
R. V. Lynch, Phillips Exeter Academy, Exeter, New Hampshire
Mary E. McDermott, Mt. Diablo Unified School District, Concord, California
W. K. McNabb, St. Mark's School of Texas, Dallas, Texas
Leila M. Maneely, Springer School, Los Altos, California
Helen M. Marston, Douglas College, New Brunswick, N.J.
L. C. Mason, Phillips University

J. R. Mayor, American Association for the Advancement of Science
Frances J. Mettler, Walter Hays Elementary School, Palo Alto, California
Muriel Mills, Hill Junior High School, Denver, Colorado
E. E. Moise, Harvard University
Max Peters, Wingate High School, Brooklyn, N.Y.
O. J. Peterson, Kansas State Teachers College
C. F. Pinzka, University of Cincinnati
H. O. Pollak, Bell Telephone Laboratories
Walter Prenowitz, Brooklyn College, Brooklyn, N.Y.
G. B. Price, University of Kansas
Persis O. Redgrave, Norwich Free Academy, Norwich, Connecticut
D. E. Richmond, Williams College, Williamstown, Massachusetts
C. E. Rickart, Yale University
P. C. Rosenbloom, University of Minnesota
Leon Rutland, University of Colorado
George Schaefer, Alexis DuPont High School, Wilmington, Delaware
Helen A. Schneider, Oak School, LaGrange, Illinois
Veryl Schult, Washington D.C. Public Schools
Willa J. Sessions, Hillsborough County Public Schools, Tampa, Florida
Leola E. Sharp, Alice Robertson Jr. High School, Muskogee, Oklahoma
Rose Mary Shea, Edith C. Baker School, Brookline, Massachusetts
M. A. Sobel, Montclair State College, Upper Montclair, N.J.
Warren Stenberg, University of Minnesota
Rothwell Stephens, Knox College, Galesburg, Illinois
Henry Swain, New Trier Township High School, Winnetka, Illinois
Wesley Thompson, Detroit Public Schools, Detroit, Michigan
G. M. Truscott, Wilbur Junior High School, Palo Alto, California
Ray Walch, Bedford Elementary School, Westport, Connecticut
R. J. Walker, Cornell University
W. C. Walsh, Saddle Brook High School, Saddle Brook, N.J.

Appendix

    Morgan Ward, California Institute of Technology
    Ted Wassam, Ventura School, Palo Alto, California
    J. F. Weaver, Boston University
    G. C. Webber, University of Deleware
    W. B. White, North High School, Sheboygan, Wisconsin
    Marie S. Wilcox, Thomas Carr Howe High School, Indianapolis, Indiana
    A. B. Willcox, Amherst College, Amherst, Massachusetts
    William Wooton, Pierce Junior College, Woodland Hills, California
    J. E. Yarnelle, Hanover College, Hanover, Indiana

25. PARTICIPANTS IN CONFERENCE ON FUTURE RESPONSIBILITIES OF SMSG, Chicago, February 1961

    A. A. Albert, University of Chicago
    Carl Allendoerfer, University of Washington
    Richard Alpert, Harvard University
    Max Beberman, University of Illinois
    E. G. Begle, Yale University
    Marlene Beigel, Cincinnati Public Schools
    R. C. Buck, University of Wisconsin
    Marion Cliffe, Los Angeles Public Schools
    Clyce L. Corcoran, Whittier (California) Public Schools
    R. P. Dilworth, California Institute of Technology
    Roy Dubisch, Fresno State College
    Howard Fehr, Columbia University
    Frederic B. Fitch, Yale University
    Robert Gagne, Princeton University
    Helen Garstens, University of Maryland
    A. M. Gleason, Harvard University
    Virginia Graham, Meridian (Mississippi) Junior College
    George Grossman, New York City Public Schools
    W. T. Guy, University of Texas
    Royce Hargrove, Corpus Christi (Texas) Public Schools
    Frank Hawthorne, New York State Dept. of Education
    Thomas J. Hill, Oklahoma City Public Schools
    J. H. Hlavaty, New York City Public Schools
    Max Hosier, Iowa State Teachers College

Lenore John, Laboratory School, University of Chicago
B. W. Jones, University of Colorado
P. S. Jones, University of Michigan
Mildred Keiffer, Cincinnati Public Schools
Norton Levy, Concord (Massachusetts) Public Schools
Frank Lindsay, California State Dept. of Education
John R. Mayor, American Association for the Advancement of Science
A. E. Meder, Rutgers University
Frances Mettler, Palo Alto (California) Public Schools
E. E. Moise, Harvard University
R. S. Pieters, Phillips Academy, Andover, Mass.
G. B. Price, University of Kansas
A. L. Putnam, University of Chicago
D. E. Richmond, Williams College
Agnes Rickey, Dade County (Florida) Public Schools
Mina Rees, Hunter College
Robert Rosenbaum, Wesleyan University
Isabelle Rucker, Virginia State Department of Education
George Springer, University of Kansas
Marshall H. Stone, University of Chicago
A. W. Tucker, Princeton University
Henry Van Engen, University of Wisconsin
John Wagner, Yale University
J. Fred Weaver, Boston University
F. Joachim Weyl, Office of Naval Research

26. MEETING TO PLAN GEOMETRY WITH COORDINATES, Princeton, March 27–31, 1961

James P. Brown, Atlanta, Georgia, Public Schools
Janet Coffman, Catonsville Senior High School, Baltimore, Maryland
A. H. Copeland, University of Michigan
W. E. Ferguson, Newton High School, Newtonville, Mass.
R. A. Good, University of Maryland
Howard Levi, Columbia University
L. A. Ringenberg, Eastern Illinois University
R. A. Rosenbaum, Wesleyan University
Harry Sitomer, New Utrecht High School, Brooklyn, N.Y.

Appendix

G. L. Spencer, Williams College
A. W. Tucker, Princeton University
C. R. Wylie, University of Utah

27. SMSG WRITING SESSION PARTICIPANTS, Summer 1961

T. A. Botts, University of Virginia
James P. Brown, Atlanta Public Schools, Georgia
Donald R. Clarkson, North Haven Junior High School, North Haven, Connecticut
Janet V. Coffman, Catonsville Senior High School, Baltimore, Maryland
Mildred B. Cole, University of Maryland
Burton H. Colvin, Boeing Scientific Research Laboratories
James A. Cooley, University of Tennessee
Arthur H. Copeland, University of Michigan
Helen L. Curran, Glenview School, Oakland, California
Margaret DeVylder, North Haven Junior High School, North Haven, Connecticut
Edwin A. Dudley, North Haven High School
W. Eugene Ferguson, Newton High School, Newtonville, Mass.
Walter Fleming, Hamline University
Harry M. Gehman, University of Buffalo
E. Glenadine Gibb, Iowa State Teachers College
Richard A. Good, University of Maryland
Geraldine Green, Vetal School, Detroit, Michigan
William T. Guy, Jr., University of Texas
Vincent H. Haag, Franklin and Marshall College
Leon Haaland, Kenwood School, Minneapolis, Minnesota
Clarence Ethel Hardgrove, Northern Illinois University
Royce S. Hargrove, Corpus Christi Public Schools, Texas
Richard R. Hartman, Edina-Morningside Senior High, Minneapolis
Thomas J. Hill, Oklahoma City Public Schools, Oklahoma City
Max Hosier, Iowa State Teachers College
Lucille Houston, Forsythe Junior High School, Ann Arbor, Michigan
Mary T. Huggins, Jordan Junior High School, Palo Alto, California

Helen L. Hughes, Theo. Roosevelt Jr. High School, Eugene, Oregon
Florence Jacobson, Albertus Magnus College, New Haven, Connecticut
Lenore John, University High School, University of Chicago
Burton W. Jones, University of Colorado
Mildred Keiffer, Cincinnati Public Schools California
David H. Knowles, Samuel Ayer High School, Milpitas, Calif.
Howard Levi, Columbia University
Emma M. Lewis, Washington, D.C. Public Schools
William G. Lister, State University of New York
Nick Lovdjieff, Anthony Junior High School, Minneapolis
Cecil McCarter, Omaha Central High School, Omaha, Nebraska
Mary McDermott, Mt. Diablo Unified School District, Concord, California
William K. McNabb, St. Mark's School, Dallas, Texas
Leila M. Maneely, Springer School, Los Altos, California
John L. Marks, San Jose State College, California
Virginia Mashin, San Diego City Schools, San Diego, California
Lysle C. Mason, Phillips University
John R. Mayor, American Association for the Advancement of Science
Frances J. Mettler, Walter Hays Elementary School, Palo Alto, California
Muriel Mills, Hill Junior High School, Denver, Colorado
John W. Murphy, Grossmont High School, Grossmont, California
William F. Oberle, Dundalk Senior High School, Dundalk, Maryland
Max Peters, Wingate High School, Brooklyn, N.Y.
Lawrence A. Ringenberg, Eastern Illinois University
Robert A. Rosenbaum, Wesleyan University
Leon Rutland, University of Colorado
Irene Sauble, Detroit Public Schools
Oscar Schaaf, South Eugene High School, Eugene, Oregon
Helen A. Schneider, Oak School, LaGrange, Illinois
Veryl Schult, Washington D.C. Public Schools
Laura Scott, Jefferson High School, Portland, Oregon

Appendix

Willa J. Sessions, Hillsborough County Public Schools, Florida
Rose Mary Shea, Edith C. Baker School, Chestnut Hill, Mass.
Harry Sitomer, New Utrecht High School, Brooklyn, N.Y.
Max A. Sobel, Montclair State College, New Jersey
Guilford L. Spencer, II, Williams College
Warren Stenberg, University of Minnesota
Ray Walch, Bedford Elementary School, Westport, Connecticut
William C. Walsh, University of Illinois
Morgan Ward, California Institute of Technology
J. Fred Weaver, Boston University
Marie S. Wilcox, Thomas Carr Howe High School, Indianapolis, Indiana
C. Raymond Wylie, University of Utah
John E. Yarnelle, Hanover College
Programed Learning Project (2-week session)
David W. Blakeslee, San Francisco State College
M. Philbrick Bridgess, Roxbury Latin School, West Roxbury, Mass.
Helen M. Jones, Oklahoma State University
William W. Matson, Portland Public Schools, Oregon
Oscar J. Peterson, Kansas State Teachers College
Persis O. Redgrave, Norwich Free Academy, Norwich, Connecticut
William A. Storer, East High School, Des Moines, Iowa
Henry Swain, New Trier Township High School, Winnetka, Illinois

28. PANEL ON PROGRAMED LEARNING

R. C. Buck, University of Wisconsin
E. E. Hammond, Phillips Academy, Andover, Massachusetts
L. D. Hawkinson, San Francisco Public Schools
J. G. Holland, Harvard University
W. J. McKeachie, University of Michigan
E. E. Moise, Harvard University
H. O. Pollak, Bell Telephone Laboratories
D. W. Taylor, Yale University

29. 1961–62 CENTERS (chairman's name is followed by consultant's)
Geometry with coordinates
Omaha, Nebraska: Duane M. Perry, Marion Heiser
Portland, Oregon: William W. Matson, Lloyd Williams
New York City: George Grossman, Myron F. Rosskopf
San Diego (California) : Frank F. Cross, Gerald A. Becker
Maryland (Baltimore) : Vincent Brant, Richard A. Good
Brooklyn, N.Y.: Harry Sitomer
Elementary
Detroit: Irene Sauble, Charles Brumfiel
Minnesota (Minneapolis) : Jack A. Lown, Fulton Koehler
Oakland (California) : Maude Coburn, James R. Smart
Boston: J. F. Weaver, chairman-consultant; Mrs. Jo Phillips, associate consultant
Peninsula (Palo Alto) : Frances J. Mettler, Paul Berg
Maryland: Helen L. Garstens, Stanley Jackson
Santa Clara County (Calif.) : Oreon Keeslar, John L. Marks
Cedar Falls: E. Glenadine Gibb, Augusta Schurrer

30. SPEAKERS AT ORIENTATION CONFERENCE, Chicago, September 23, 1961

E. G. Begle, Director, SMSG
J. P. Brown, Atlanta Public Schools
Janet V. Coffman, Catonsville Senior High School, Baltimore, Maryland
W. E. Ferguson, Newton High School, Newtonville, Massachusetts
R. A. Good, University of Maryland
Virginia Mashin, San Diego City Schools, San Diego, California
J. W. Murphy, Grossmont High School, Grossmont, California
W. F. Oberle, Dundalk Senior High School, Dundalk, Maryland
L. A. Ringenberg, Eastern Illinois University
R. A. Rosenbaum, Wesleyan University
Laura Scott, Jefferson High School, Portland, Oregon
G. L. Spencer, Williams College, Williamstown, Massachusetts
C. R. Wylie, University of Utah

Appendix

31. AD HOC COMMITTEE ON BYLAWS

   J. H. Hlavaty, Dewitt Clinton High School, New York
   J. R. Mayor, American Association for the Advancement of Science
   E. E. Moise, Harvard University

32. PANEL ON TESTS

   R. Alpert, Harvard University
   Max Beberman, University of Illinois
   R. P. Dilworth, California Institute of Technology
   J. Kagan, The Fels Research Institute, Yellow Springs, Ohio
   M. A. Linton, Jr., William Penn Charter School, Philadelphia, Pennsylvania
   W. G. Lister, State University of New York

33. PANEL ON SMALL PUBLICATIONS

   R. D. Anderson, Louisiana State University
   M. P. Bridgess, Roxbury Latin School, West Roxbury, Massachusetts
   J. M. Calloway, Kalamazoo College, Kalamazoo, Michigan
   R. J. Clark, St. Paul's School, Concord, New Hampshire
   Roy Dubisch, University of Washington
   T. H. Hill, Oklahoma City Schools
   K. S. Kalman, Lincoln High School, Philadelphia, Pennsylvania
   Augusta L. Schurrer, Iowa State Teachers College, Cedar Falls, Iowa
   Henry W. Syer, Kent School, Kent, Connecticut

34. COMMITTEE ON SPANISH TRANSLATIONS

   Howard F. Fehr, Columbia University
   Mariano Garcia, University of Puerto Rico, Mayaguez, P.R.
   Max Kraemer, San Jose State College, San Jose, California

35. PARTICIPANTS AT THE CONFERENCE ON MATHEMATICAL FILMS, Chicago, June 1-3, 1963

Frank B. Allen, Lyons Township High School, LaGrange, Illinois
Henry M. Alder, University of California at Davis
Max Beberman, University of Illinois
E. G. Begle, Stanford University
Emil J. Berger, St. Paul Public Schools, Minnesota
Kenneth E. Brown, U.S. Office of Education
M. Brydegaard, San Diego State College, San Diego, California
R. Creighton Buck, University of Wisconsin
Arnold M. Chandler, Department of Public Instruction, Madison, Wisconsin
Leon W. Cohen, University of Maryland
Ralph B. Crouch, New Mexico State University
Robert C. Fisher, Ohio State University
M. K. Fort, Jr., University of Georgia
David Gale, Brown University
Harry M. Gehman, University of Buffalo
E. Glenadine Gibb, Iowa State Teachers College
Richard A. Good, University of Maryland
Julius H. Hlavaty, De Witt Clinton School, New York City
M. Gweneth Humphreys, Randolph-Macon Woman's College
Bernard Jacobson, Franklin and Marshall College
Burton W. Jones, University of Colorado
P. S. Jones, University of Michigan
John L. Kelley, University of California
Holbrook M. MacNeille, Case Institute of Technology
Julian D. Mancill, University of Alabama
Kenneth O. May, Carleton College
Richard Paulson, National Science Foundation
Richard S. Pieters, Phillips Academy, Andover, Mass.
Henry O. Pollak, Bell Telephone Laboratories
G. Baley Price, University of Kansas
Joseph A. Raab, Wisconsin State College
Charles E. Rickart, Yale University
Agnes Y. Rickey, Dade County Board of Public Instruction, Florida
Paul C. Rosenbloom, University of Minnesota

Appendix

    Isabelle P. Rucker, Virginia State Department of Education
    Harry D. Ruderman, Hunter College High School, New York City
    Leonard Simon, Bronx, N.Y.
    A. W. Tucker, Princeton University
    Elbridge P. Vance, Oberlin College
    Robert J. Wisner, Michigan State University Oakland
    Leo Zippin, Queen's College, Flushing, N.Y.

36. MEMBERS OF INTERIM CENTRAL COORDINATING COMMITTEE FOR FILMS

    A. M. Chandler, State Department of Public Instruction, Madison, Wisconsin
    R. C. Fisher, Ohio State University
    J. H. Hlavaty, DeWitt Clinton High School, New York City
    M. Gweneth Humphreys, Randolph-Macon Woman's College
    H. M. MacNeille, Case Institute of Technology
    H. D. Ruderman, Hunter College High School, New York City
    E. P. Vance, Oberlin College

37. COMMITTEE ON GIFTED STUDENTS

    Roy Dubisch, University of Washington
    Robert C. Fisher, Ohio State University
    R. E. K. Rourke, Kent School, Kent, Connecticut
    A. W. Tucker, Princeton University
    Marie S. Wilcox, Thomas Carr Howe High School, Indianapolis (chairman)

38. TEXTBOOK WITHDRAWAL COMMITTEE

    Frank B. Allen, Lyons Township High School, LaGrange, Illinois
    Stewart S. Cairns, Chairman, University of Illinois
    Mildred Keiffer, Cincinnati Public Schools
    G. Baley Price, University of Kansas

Index

AMS. *See* American Mathematical Society

Administrative staff of SMSG. *See* Staff of SMSG

Administrative structure of SMSG, 14

Administrators, school, 4, 5, 138

Advanced placement program, 6

Advisory Board. *See* Advisory Committee

Advisory Committee: groups and areas represented on, 14; appointment of, 14; appoints Panel on 7th and 8th grades, 48; first formal meeting of, 48; need for attention to elementary school mathematics, 54; meetings, 55, 56, 93, 133; recommendation of, on elementary school mathematics, 56, 89; interest in psychological research, 57; activities during *1959–60* academic year, 92–94; reviews sample textbooks, 92; suggests alternate version of geometry, 93; advises on writers for *1960*, 95; begins receiving progress reports, 97; appoints committee on bylaws, 111; suggests study of programed learning, 121; becomes Advisory Board, 128; activities during *1961–62* academic year, 133; members of original, 148

Algebra: as topic for 9th grade, 25, 84; in 11th grade sample textbooks, 85

American Association for the Advancement of Science, 16

American Mathematical Society: urged to act on mathematics curriculum, 10; nature of, 11; as founder of MAA, 11; main concern of, 12; action by council of, 12

Anderson, Richard D., 113

Angell Hall, 65

Applications of mathematics: in traditional textbooks, 21; necessity of concepts before, 108; relative importance of, 141f.

Articulation: of SMSG textbooks,

173

Articulation *(Continued)* 39; committee appointed for, 98
Attitudes, students', toward mathematics, 5, 95

Beberman, Max, 7
Beckenbach, Edwin F., 74, 132
Begle, Edward G., 13, 15ff., 40ff., 54ff., 58, 62, 68, 78, 88ff., 93ff., 98, 105, 112, 114f., 121ff., 144
Bell Telephone Laboratories, 16
Bellman, Richard, 132
Birkhoff, G. D., 32
Branford College, 116
Branner Hall, 97
Brauer, Richard, 12
Bylaws of SMSG: suggested, 111; adopted by Advisory Committee, 128; nature of 12ff.; published, 129

CEEB. *See* College Entrance Examination Board
CUPM. *See* Committee on the Undergraduate Program
Calculus: Commission on Mathematics position on, 36; SMSG position on, 37
Cambridge Conference, 11, 146
Cedar Hall, 126
Centers, tryout: organization of *(1958)*, 46; effectiveness of, 46f.; selection of chairmen for, 47; distribution of material to, 54; for *1959–60* academic year, 59, 87; conflicting reports from, 63; reports used at *1960* writing session, 97; for programed material, 122; for *1961–62* academic year, 127; for Spanish language project, 131; location of, 150, 156f., 168
Chapter team, 72
Chicago Conference on Research Potential and Training, 9
College Entrance Examination Board: advanced placement program, 6; Committee on Examinations, 7; Commission on Mathematics, 8, 15, 18, 24, 29, 34, 36f., 40, 51, 94
Commission on Mathematics: establishment of, 8; report of, 8; appendices to report of, 8; represented on SMSG Advisory Committee, 14; representatives of, on SMSG writing teams, 18; use of report of, by SMSG, 24, 40; position on high school mathematics courses, 29, 34, 36f.; proposal for geometry, 94
Commission on Reorganization of the Secondary School, 2
Committee on Bylaws, 128
Committee of Eight, 12ff., 48, 147
Committee on Elementary School Mathematics, 56
Committee on Examinations of CEEB, 7
Committee on Gifted Students, 133, 171
Committee on Psychology, 95, 159
Committees of SMSG: advisory, 14; executive, 15; on Elementary School Mathematics, 56; on Psychology, 95; on Bylaws, 128. *See also* Panels of SMSG.

Index

Committee of Ten, 2
Committee on the Undergraduate Program of the Mathematical Association of America, 52, 137
Concepts of Informal Geometry, 113
Conference(s) of SMSG: Chicago, on Research Potential and Training, 9; Mathematics Meeting of NSF (Cambridge), 10; orientation, for *1958* tryout teachers, 48; on Elementary School Mathematics, 56, 95; orientation, for *1959* tryout teachers, 89; on Future Responsibilities of SMSG, 110f.; proceedings of, printed and bound, 126; orientation, for *1961* tryout teachers, 127f.; on mathematical films, 131; speakers at, 151, 153, 157, 168; participants at, 145, 146, 163, 170
Conference Board of the Mathematical Sciences, 111
Consultants for tryout centers, 46
Contest Problem Book, The, 132
Cooley, J. A., 99
Council of the AMS, 12
Crowder, N. A., 120
Cubberly Education Building, 126
Curriculum: traditional mathematics, 2; of UICSM, 7; of Commission on Mathematics, 8; other studies of the mathematical, 9; textbooks as factors influencing, 21; traditional junior high school, 21; for non-college-bound students, 91;

long-term study of, 129. *See also* High school curriculum, Sample textbooks
Curtis, C. W., 53

Daus, Paul H., 53
Davis, Philip J., 132
Davis Robert, 89
Deductive reasoning: in high school geometry, 29; in 7th and 8th grade sample textbooks, 83; in 9th grade sample textbooks, 84
Discovery: built into 9th grade textbooks, 84; used in elementary school textbooks, 119f.
Draftsmen: for *1959* writing session, 59, 62; for *1960* writing session, 103

Editorial Committee of Panel on Monographs, 51
Educational Testing Service, 109
Elementary Functions, 37, 75, 85
Elementary school mathematics: extension of SMSG's work to, 54; content in sample textbooks for, 119
Elementary school mathematics writing subgroup: problems facing, 99; steering committee for, 99; operating procedures, 99f.; consult earlier work, 100; use immediate classroom tryout, 100; activities at *1961* writing session, 118f.
Eleventh grade writing subgroup: chairman of, 33; problems faced by, 34ff.; goals of, 35;

175

Eleventh grade *(Continued)*
meeting in Chicago *(1959)*, 55;
activities at *1959* writing session, 71ff.; operating procedures, 71–73; use of chapter teams, 72
Ellingwood, Robert, 68, 79
Elliott, Mrs. Ella, 115
Evaluation of sample textbooks, 96, 107ff.
Executive Committee, 14, 15, 93

Fleming, Walter, 102

Geometry, 113
Geometry: criticism of traditional, 30ff.; as topics of 10th grade mathematics, 29; SMSG approach to, 32; alternative version of, 93f. *See also* Geometry-with-Coordinates writing subgroup
Geometric Inequalities, 132
Geometry-with-Coordinates writing subgroup: proposed, 93f.; writers acquired, 112; holds planning session, 112; operating procedures, 116f.
Gifted students, committee on, 133, 171
Goals of SMSG, 11, 18, 19, 20, 49, 136
Grants to SMSG, 13, 14, 45, 97, 107

Haag, Vincent, 70n., 92, 113
Hargrove, Royce, 105
Headquarters of SMSG: moves to Boulder temporarily, 78; moves from Yale to Stanford, 115
Heinecke, Philip, 95
Henry Barnard Hall, 45
High school, recent history of, 1ff.
High school curriculum, changing nature of, 2
High school mathematics teachers: as SMSG writers, 16; relationship with mathematicians, 17, 38, 42; poorly trained, 52; in-service training of, 52, for tryout centers, 88; reactions to SMSG, 136
Housing at summer writing sessions: in *1958,* 17, 38; in *1959,* 63; in *1960,* 97; in *1961,* 116

Inductive reasoning, 83
In-service teacher training: as concern of SMSG, 52; production of films for, 131f.
Institutes: NSF as sponsor of, 52; need for, 52
Interim Central Coordinating Committee, 131
Interim writing: for grades 7 and 8, 54; for grade 10, 55; for grade 11, 55; for grade 12, 55
Intermediate Mathematics, 85
Introduction to Inequalities, 132
Introduction to Matrix Algebra, 73, 75, 86

Jones, Burton W., 79
Junior High School Mathematics, 67: teacher's commentary for, 67; content of, 67

Kazarinoff, Nicholas D., 132

Index

Keiffer, Mildred, 101
Kutuzov, B. V., 113

Lax, Anneli, 112
Learning mathematics: problems of, 54; SMSG research in, 95
Leet Oliver Hall, 44
Liaison with universities, 68, 95
Long's Peak, 69
Long-term study of new mathematics curricula, 129
Lore of Large Numbers, The, 132
Luce, R. D., 53

MAA. *See* Mathematical Association of America
Mathematical Association of America: as factor in formation of SMSG, 10; jointly sponsors conference on mathematical films, 131
Mathematical concepts, importance of, 108f.
Mathematical skills, importance of, 107f.
Mathematics Film Center, 131
Mathematics Meeting of the NSF, 10f.
Mathematician(s): relationship with high school teachers, 6, 13, 17, 18, 38, 42, 66; responsibilities of, on writing teams, 23, 33; as consultants for teachers, 46, 88; on Panel on Monographs, 51; on Editorial Committee, 51; collaboration of, with elementary school teachers, 100; prepare objectives for programed materials, 122; reaction of, to SMSG, 141ff.
Matrix algebra, as topic for sample textbook, 73
Mayor, John, 21, 22
Minnesota National Laboratory for the Improvement of Secondary Mathematics, 110
Modern algebra, as topic for sample textbook, 37
Moise, E. E., 55, 70, 71

NCTM. *See* National Council of Teachers of Mathematics
NSF. *See* National Science Foundation
National Council of Teachers of Mathematics: as factor in formation of SMSG, 10; represented on Advisory Committee, 15; members receive first Newsletter, 57; jointly sponsor conference on mathematical films, 131
National Science Foundation: as conference sponsor, 9, 10; Mathematics Meeting of the, 10; grants to SMSG, 13, 45, 97, 107; as sponsor of institutes, 52; progress reports to, 97; sanctions move from Yale to Stanford, 115
New Mathematical Library, 51
Newsletter(s): objectives of SMSG listed in, 49; publication of begins, 57; during *1959–60* academic year, 96; test results published in, 109f.

177

Nine-M writing subgroup. *See* Non-college-bound high school writing subgroup.
Ninth-grade writing subgroup: chairman of, 25; content of, 25; operating procedures, 25ff., 69f.; problems faced by, 26ff.; interim writing by, 54, 55; at *1959* writing session, 69f.
Niven, Ivan, 132
Non-college-bound high school writing subgroup: begins work, 102; operating procedures, 102f.; format of sample textbook produced by, 103; at *1961* writing session, 118.
Non-college-bound junior high school writing subgroup: begins work, 101; operating procedures, 102; at *1961* writing session, 117f.
Non-college-bound student(s): as concern of SMSG, 56; definition of, 90; appointment of Panel on, 90; problems associated with, 90ff.; experimental classes using, 91
Numbers: Rational and Irrational, 132

Objectives of SMSG. *See* Goals of SMSG

PSSC. *See* Physical Science Study Committee
Panel on Elementary School Mathematics: proposed by Advisory Committee, 56; appointed, 89; aids in planning textbooks, 99; activities during *1960–61* academic year, 113f.; meets to do interim writing, 127f.; members of, 158
Panel on Monographs: appointment of, 49; responsibilities of, 50; Editorial Committee of, 51; activities during *1959–60* academic year, 94; makes arrangements with commercial publishers, 94; work load increases, 111; membership made rotating, 111; members of, 152
Panel on Non-College-Bound Students: appointed, 90; responsibilities of, 90f.; first meeting of, 90; activities during *1960–61* academic year, 113; members of, 159
Panel on Programed Learning: appointed, 121; first meeting of, 121; responsibilities of, 130; members of, 167
Panel on Sample Textbooks: appointment of, 49; responsibilities of, 50; first meeting of, 50; activities during 1959–60 academic year, 92; acquires new member, 112; members of, 152
Panel on Seventh and Eighth Grades: appointment of, 48; responsibilities of, 50; first meeting of, 50; meeting prior to *1959* writing session, 63; activities during *1959–60* academic year, 92; ceases operations, 112; members of, 151

Index

Panel on Small Publications: announced, 129; responsibilities of, 130; members of, 169
Panel on Teacher Training: appointment of, 50; responsibilities of, 52; relationship with CUPM, 52; publications sponsored by, 53; activities during *1959–60* academic year, 92; activities during *1960–61* academic year, 113; members of, 152
Panel on Tests: announced, 129; responsibilities of, 129; members of, 169
Physical Science Study Committee: as pioneer curriculum study group, 11; monographs published by, **51**
Point (s): as variation of tryout center, 87; in *1961–62,* 127; paying, 127
Pre-algebra course, 21
Pre-service teacher training, 52
Printing of sample textbooks: typing problems involved in, 78f.; sites of, 82; plans for in *1960,* 96f.; during *1960–61,* 105
Programed learning: description of, 120; SMSG begins work with, 120
Psychology: SMSG's concern with, 56; SMSG begins work with, 95f.
Public relations: need for, 53, 54; SMSG begins program in, 57; Newsletters as, 57; avenues employed by SMSG, 58; during *1959–60* academic year, 96

RAND Corporation, 16
Random House, 94, 112, 132
Reaction to SMSG: by students, 135f.; by teachers, 136; by teacher-training institutions, 136f.; by parents, 137f.; by school administrators, 138f.; by mathematicians, 141ff.
Reading difficulties, effect on textual material, 4
Recreation for writers, 69
Rees, Mina, 10
Remedial mathematics courses, 4
Report of Commission on Mathematics, 8
Revision of SMSG textbooks, 97f.
Richmond, Donald E., 36
Roehr, George, 115
Rosenbaum, R. A., 112
Rosenbloom, Paul C., 110
Russian mathematics, translation of, by SMSG, 92

Salkind, Charles T., 132
Sample textbooks: purpose of, 19, 20; consistency of viewpoint in, 39; articulation of, 39, 98; Panel on, 49, 50, 92, 112, 152; printing of, 59, 96, 106, 124ff.; time devoted to writing, 75; difficulty of writing, 76; criticism of during writing, 76ff.; content of 7th and 8th grade, 83f.; content of 9th grade, 84; content of 10th grade, 84f.; content of 11th grade, 85; content of 12th grade, 85f.; as media for changing curriculum, 86; comparison with traditional textbooks, 86f.,

179

Sample textbooks *(Continued)* 108; format of, 86f.; as a synthesis of opinion, 92f.; overlap in content of, 98; content of elementary school, 100; standardizing symbols in, 99; for 7-M students, 101; for 9-M students, 102; sales of, 106, 125; distribution of, 106; reduction in size of, 106; testing of, 107; withdrawal from sale of, 106f., 133f.; alternate geometry begun, 112

Sawyer, W. W., 132

Saybrook College, 116

School and College Study for Admission with Advanced Standing, 6

Set concepts, overlap in treatment of in sample textbooks, 40

Seven cardinal principles of secondary education, 2, 3

Seventh and eighth grade writing subgroup: chairman of, 21; problems faced by, 21; use of UMMaP materials, 22; goals of, 22; operating procedures, 22ff.; activities at *1959* writing session, 63ff.; activities at *1960* writing session, 98; activities at *1961* writing session, 117

Singer, L. W., Co., 132

Skills, mathematical, 3, 107f.

Skinner, B. F., 120

Smith, Leander, 122

Some Basic Mathematical Concepts, 53

Spanish: translation of SMSG materials into, 130; Committee on, 169

Sputnik I, 9

Staff of SMSG: growth of, 44, 45; problems facing, 54; organization of duplication services, 79; enlarged, 89, 105, 115; changes caused by move to Stanford, 115

Stevens, John W., 79n.

Stevens, Mrs. Phyllis, 16, 115

Structure of Elementary Algebra, 113

Studies in Mathematics, sponsored by SMSG, 53

Study Guide in Modern Algebra, 53

Summer writing session (s)

(1958): plans for, 13; securing writers for, 15; housing for, 17; opening of, 18; subgroups of, 19ff.; personality of, 37, 42; termination of, 41; results of, 41; resolutions adopted by, 42

(1959): plans for, 53; testing experts for, 62, 75; draftsmen for, 62; two sessions to be held, 58; securing writers for, 58, 59; housing for, 63, 68; recreation for writers at, 79f.; results of, 80, 82

(1960): plans for, 94ff.; housing for, 97; opening of, 97; activities at, 97ff.

(1961): plans for, 115; opening of, 115f.; housing for, 116; activities at, 116ff.

(1962), 134

Swain, Henry, 25

Index

Symbolism in SMSG textbooks, 26ff., 99

"Talks to Teachers," in SMSG teacher's commentaries, 85
Teacher's commentaries: for 7th and 8th grade textbooks, 66, 67; for 9th grade textbook, 70; for 10th grade textbook, 71; for 11th grade textbook, 73; for 12th grade textbook, 74; inclusion of tests in, 75; "Talks to Teachers" in, 85
Teacher training: Panel on, 50; need for in-service, 52; preservice, as concern of CUPM, 52
Tenth grade writing subgroup: chairman of, 29; problems facing, 29ff.; operating procedures, 33; activities at *1959* writing session, 70f.
Testing experts, at SMSG writing sessions, 62, 75, 103
Testing sample textbooks: by Educational Testing Service, 109; by Minnesota National Laboratory, 110; results published in Newsletters, 109
Traditional mathematics textbooks, 4, 87, 107ff.
Trancos House, 97
Trigonometry: criticism of traditional, 34; in SMSG 11th grade textbook, 35, 85; in SMSG 12th grade textbook, 85f.
Trumbull College, 40
Tryout of sample textbooks: as part of SMSG's responsibilities, 46; procedure for, 46; duties of center chairmen, 46; selection of center chairmen, 47; 7th and 8th grade units, 54; centers for, 59, 60, 87, 127; conference for teachers of, 89
Tucker, A. W., 8
Turkish Society for Pure and Applied Mathematics, 133
Twelfth grade writing subgroup: chairman of, 36; problems faced by, 36; goals of, 37; interim work by, 55; activities at *1959* writing session, 73ff.; operating procedures, 73ff.
Tryouts for SMSG, 79, 82, 103

UICSM. *See* university of Illinois Committee on School Mathematics
UMMaP. *See* University of Maryland Mathematics Project
University of Illinois Committee on School Mathematics, 7, 15, 18, 24, 27, 40
University of Maryland Mathematics Project, 18, 21, 22, 40, 48
Uses of Infinity, The, 132

Vroman, A. C., Co., 132

Wagner, John, 58, 78, 89, 105, 114
Walker, Robert J., 29, 53
Wesleyan University Press, 94, 111
What is Calculus About?, 132
Withdrawal of sample textbooks from sale: procedures for, 133f.; committee for, 171

Writers at SMSG writing sessions: securing, 14, 15; groups represented by, 16, 18; housing of, 17, 38, 63, 97, 116; working hours of, 40; relationships between, 42, 43; optimum use of, 66, 76; recreation for, 69, 79f.; inclusion of experienced writers among, 75f.; names of, 149, 153–55, 160–62, 165–67

Writing subgroups: for *1958* writing session, 19, 25; coordination between, 19, 22; functions of chairmen of, 191; methods of operation, 23; working hours of, 40; reference materials available for, 40. *See also* Seventh and Eighth grade, Ninth grade, Tenth grade, Eleventh grade, Twelfth grade, Elementary school, and Non-college-bound writing subgroups

Yale Clerical Bureau, 54, 59
Yale University Press, 59, 106, 124, 125, 132

Zippin, Leo, 132

QA
11
.W74

Date Due